'ALLO 'ALLO!

THE WAR DIARIES
OF RENÉ ARTOIS

Translated by John Haselden

Based on the
BBC Television series
by Jeremy Lloyd and
David Croft

BBC Books

TO TERENCE

Published by BBC Books,
a division of BBC Enterprises Limited
Woodlands, 80 Wood Lane, London W12 0TT
First published 1988
Reprinted 1989 (twice)

ISBN 0 563 20688 8

Cover and page design concept:
Grub Street Design, London
Art director: Roger Hammond
Designer: Debbie George
French artwork: John Davis

All photographs are BBC © except for the following:
page 102 (top) POPPERFOTO, page 103 (top) REX FEATURES.

Set in 11 on 13 point Century Bold
Printed and bound in Great Britain by Butler
& Tanner Ltd, Frome, Somerset
Cover printed by Belmont Press Ltd,
Northampton

ACKNOWLEDGMENTS

No masterpiece of this size can be credited to one man. Much of what appears within the pages of this journal could not have been achieved without my mother. To her I owe my thanks for her tireless energy, her intimate memories of the principal players in this drama, her personal selection of photographs and permission to reveal the extraordinary contents of the knockwurst.

To the firm of Gruber Geering Von Strohm (Fine Arts), Buenos Aires, I am grateful for permission to reproduce the painting of The Fallen Madonna with the Big Boobies – a prominent feature of the poster for the Tate Gallery 1946 Van Clomp Retrospective (pp. 144–5), and a page from the original manuscript of Odes for a Nancy Boy by Hubert Gruber (p. 52).

Thanks, too, are due to the Nouvion District Council for their support of the project and their loan of much archive material.

This diary could not have been published in this shape without the support of Sheila Ableman, which is enormous, or the help of Martyn Forrester and Mark Lucas (and Evie and Mindy, who serve under them).

As for the legendary René Artois himself, my debt, like France's, can never truly be repaid. His text, on the whole, needs little embellishment, but I have decorated it with much evocative memorabilia from his own private collection, and although he never intended this work for publication during his lifetime, I feel sure it captures the essence of that giant among men.

René Fairfax
London 1988

INTRODUCTION

I never met René Artois, although even before the discovery of these priceless papers I felt I had known him almost as a father.

My mother Yvette spoke about him often, of course. They fought side by side in those terrible years during the war, to free themselves from the yoke of the oppressor. And even when René's wife was not there, there were the Germans to worry about.

We share the same name. But there is more to it than that. We share the same spirit. As I left my job at the Bank of Westphalia each evening to study these diaries and arrange them for publication, I would feel the stirrings of adventure. Even so, I went straight back to my rooms and read more of René's entries, and was sometimes up late into the night.

Though these pages are shot through with his characteristic modesty, there emerges, as my mother said, something remarkable, something incredible.

Consider his position. My mother often did. At the beginning of the war, he was, like many young Frenchmen, in his mid-forties. Vital, attractive, blessed with unbounded energy and courage, he dreamed of

military service. Fortunately, someone was always there to wake him with a large cognac and remind him that he was already serving France in the best way he could. There were so many who depended upon him.

There was his wife, Edith, for a start. Although it is typical of René's generosity that she rarely came first. There was her mother, Fanny, lying desperately sick in a bed upstairs. He was constantly trying to think of ways to ease her passing. There were Carstairs and Fairfax*, the British airmen, who would be lucky to get out of the Café René alive. And there was Maria, my mother Yvette, and so many others. No matter what he had on, he would always do his best to look after them personally. He was that sort of man.

Seen in this light, it is even more extraordinary that he managed at once to keep his end up with the Resistance, to handle the Germans and to keep in good spirits all those who came to drink at his café.

René Artois passed away in 1985, and my mother, who was with him, told me with a wistful smile that he died as he had lived. He amassed a considerable fortune in later years. Not only did the hotel trade reward him handsomely, but after the war he also developed widespread and varied business interests. His dealings in the world of fine art and cuckoo clocks alone took him as far afield as Switzerland and South America.

It surprised me to learn, therefore, that his sole bequest to my mother was a rather mature knockwurst sausage, which had hung in his cellar since late 1945. My mother, however, could not have been more pleased. With a twinkle in her eye she said simply: 'He wanted me to have a little something to remember him by.' Little? That

---

* *Fairfax finally escaped to England in 1973. René had been telling him for years that the war was over, but for some reason he carried on hiding in and around the café through the fifties and sixties. He was there so long that my mother eventually married him out of sympathy and, as a result, I bear the unfortunate man's surname. I keep meaning to have it changed.*

sausage must have been a metre long. And then I understood. René Artois could have left Yvette jewellery; he could have left her money; but he chose instead to leave her a piece of history. Not for him the easy gesture.

How much history I was only to find out some years later. By that time his exploits had become legendary in France, and also in some areas of England, through television. It was in April of last year, I remember, that I stayed late one night at the office, working with one of the

René Artois in the process of changing history

secretaries. She was a young girl and had much to learn, so I did not arrive home until after midnight. For some reason I still had an incredible appetite, so I went immediately to the kitchen of my mother. Alas, she had been entertaining, so René's sausage was the only thing in the larder.

I looked upon it as I often had, with respect, mixed with a certain awe. It really was a magnificent sausage, despite its age. I thought again, he must have been a remarkable man. But I was hungry and, as René himself would have said: 'When a Frenchman hungers, he must satisfy himself.' So I took that sausage, and cut myself a large slice. I must say that first mouthful tasted good. As I chewed it over, however, I detected a certain fibrous texture which, though not unpleasant, meant that my dinner lasted rather longer than I had planned. On closer inspection of the remainder of the sausage, I suddenly saw why.

Mon Dieu!

I called my mother.

It was an emotional scene. When she came upon René's sausage, now, sadly, shorter by some ten centimetres, it brought tears to her eyes.

'Mother,' I said, 'what is it?'

She, too, looked more closely, and saw that the knockwurst was not what it seemed. Concealed beneath its greying skin was a work of art of inestimable value.

'René!' she cried. 'You have just taken a very large nibble out of the Fallen Madonna with the Big Boobies by Van Clomp!'

But no.

I had consumed several thousand words of the first volume of *The War Diaries of René Artois*, which sharp-sighted readers will realise explains certain unfortunate gaps in the text that follows.

The rest, of course, is history.

René Fairfax
September 1988

1 JANUARY

What an evening! Awoke with a very stiff

my dear Edith

sharp tap with a metal spoon

dropped off.

Yvette in the airing cupboard up against the tank.*

---

* *This page is considerably damaged. It is clear from the evidence that remains, however, that René began the year as he meant to go on. He was a man of great stamina. Aroused after the night's traditional festivities, he discovers a large cognac on his bedside table. Why it is stiff can only be guessed at, though my mother recalls that he promised to give her one the previous day and wanted it close to hand.*

In any event, we move on with a word or two of culinary advice from Le Grand Chef to his lady wife, before he decides to have a little lie-in.

The entry concludes with René and Yvette making a bold attack on a Panzer. From the upstairs bathroom of the café it would have been possible for René to lob a grenade through the skylight and down into the street. He must have asked my mother to help prime his weapon in the airing cupboard prior to launching a vigorous assault.

2 JANUARY

and most of the day sleeping it off. I hope, dear diary, that this is not a sign of things to come.

But what sort of year will it be, I wonder, under the tyranny of the jackboot? The British are not coming to rescue me, or they would be here by now. And they wouldn't know what to do with Edith either.

So, times are hard, and I have to console myself, and Yvette and Maria when I have the strength, with the knowledge that I am giving my all for France.

I own a café which is being used by the Resistance for hiding two escaped airmen. It is dangerous, I know, but I insisted.

I still have to be nice to the Germans. They are my customers. Also, they are winning the war, despite my efforts, and if I cross them they will shoot me. I care little for myself, of course, but so many others depend on my enormous support.

I have to be nice to my wife, because if she finds out I'm having

with Yvette and sometimes have to comfort Maria too, she will shoot me.*

Everyone seems to know about the airmen, except my wife's mother, permanently bed-ridden in the attic – and up to now I've had a better relationship with the Gestapo. Edith knows about them. Leclerc, the ex-jailbird and forger, knows about them. Even Colonel Von Strohm, the Commandant of Nouvion, knows about them.

I worry about the Colonel – but fortunately I know his secret. He and Captain Geering have concealed the painting of The Fallen Madonna with the Big Boobies by Van Clomp in a knockwurst sausage which is hanging in my cellar. It is supposed to be a present for Hitler, but I know they hope to sell it after the war.

I worry about Lieutenant Gruber. I know his secret as well, only with that cologne he wears it's not much of a secret.

I worry about Michelle of the Resistance. She keeps popping out from behind the curtains in the back room with a gun, just when the urge to perform my duty with Yvette overwhelms me.

---

* It is difficult to tell why Edith has threatened René's life, especially since he is always ready to do his bit for France. Was she jealous of my mother? Very possibly. Yvette is referred to admiringly during the course of a great number of René's entries. Her desire for action in the most dangerous circumstances seems almost to have matched his own.

3 FEBRUARY

A terrible tragedy has occurred. Posterity has been denied an account of my incredible achievements for over a month!

I was in the cellar with Yvette, building a wall to conceal the painting of The Fallen Madonna with the Big Boobies by Van Clomp, and I accidentally hid my diary as well. We were disturbed by Edith just as I was putting the last brick in, and it must have slipped out of my trouser pocket.

I sometimes wonder whether I am the only hero of the Resistance in all France who takes the trouble to do a good job. Ah well, at least Yvette seems to appreciate it.

'You are the most exciting man I have ever laid with,' she said as we were nearly finished. How could I respond, in all modesty, and with a trowel full of wet cement in one hand? 'It is getting hard,' I said. 'And I must get it in immediately.'

I'm glad to say Edith understood why I had to wipe my filthy hands on Yvette's blouse, once I had explained the subterfuge. If Otto Flick of the Gestapo had caught me building a wall he would have been immediately suspicious.

I nipped down to the cellar yesterday evening to help Maria out, and found my priceless memoir in a very dark corner. My excitement was short-lived, but then that's often the way with Maria. All too soon Michelle of the Resistance appeared like a phantom out of the night with some disturbing news.

'She is in the back room,' Edith announced to me in front of a room full of German officers. 'Shall I sing a song to distract everyone?'

I told her it was not necessary. Although the singing of my wife is always very good for the sales of the cheese I can't help thinking that if it goes on we will start to lose customers.

Maria was at a table, attending to Lieutenant Gruber.

She must have been planning a quiet night in. 'I want you in the back,' I said.

'A little note would have been more discreet,' Gruber replied with that little smile of his that I find so alarming. Since his experiences on the Russian Front he's never quite lost the need for shared bodily warmth. The Russian Front was a very cold front. When I escaped with Maria to talk to Michelle, however, it suddenly seemed very appealing.

'I have information that you are to be interrogated by the Germans,' she said. 'They are ruthless men, and may even take your wife and torture her in front of you.'

What could I do but grit my teeth bravely. 'I will tell them nothing,' I said.

Michelle gave me a ring with a death pill in the clasp, in case I couldn't stand the pain. Then Colonel Von Strohm gave me a ring and told me to appear at his HQ immediately. Courageously, I told him that it would not be possible. I had to think of the café, the kitchen, my many responsibilities, and my bicycle which had a puncture. *Mon Dieu*, how I fought!

When he offered to send an armoured car, I put the phone down and ordered my walking boots and some sandwiches for the next morning's journey. The château requisitioned by the Germans wasn't far, but I thought I might take the scenic route.

6 FEBRUARY

Helga, the personal assistant of the Colonel, was very stern when she showed me in to his office yesterday. Some men like that, but I had more important things on my mind and a bottle of Château Lafite '37 in my pocket. Perhaps Helga thought it was meant for her.

But it wasn't. It was for Von Strohm, along with the cigars, a few cheeses and a Napoleon cognac I had cunningly brought as a diversion. For Helga, there was perfume.

It didn't work. No sooner had I handed over these gifts, than Captain Geering asked for a pair of pliers and a rubber hose. I won't say I wasn't appalled. I was. My whole life flashed before my eyes, and particularly the early days of my marriage to Edith. I may even have offered to tell them everything.

Thankfully, they just needed these things to mend the gas poker.

'René,' the Colonel spat, 'we know you are hiding two British airmen for the Resistance, and I am going to have you shot.'

Typically, I stood firm, and mentioned the painting of

The Fallen Madonna with the Big Boobies by Van Clomp in my cellar. The Colonel was not made of such stern stuff. He said he planned to hand the painting over to Otto Flick of the Gestapo, so that they would leave him in peace. For some reason he planned to hand me over as well. As a gesture of friendship and respect he gave me a ring with a death pill in the clasp.

'Perhaps you would like to give your wife one?' suggested the Captain. I could see that my reputation preceded me.

'Even a Frenchman cannot think of that sort of thing at a time like this,' I said.

He felt it might provide the only way out. I thought I'd try to find some others. I outlined a plan of great brilliance and audacity. We would get Leclerc, the forger, to make a copy of The Fallen Madonna with the Big Boobies. This we would give to the Gestapo whilst keeping the original to sell after the war. For his trouble, I had a hunch Leclerc would accept little more than a Château Lafite '37, some cigars, a Napoleon cognac and some perfume.

The cheese they could keep for my wife's next cabaret performance.

On my return to the café I went instantly to the cellar with Yvette. I resolved to keep the full details of my ordeal from her. There are some things even a Frenchman will not reveal in front of a woman.

'It was a nightmare. I never thought I would get out alive.'

'Oh René,' Yvette breathed, 'you are so brave. When you were there I lit candles.'

'You were praying for me?' I was touched, as I often am by this innocent, vulnerable girl.

'We had a power cut.'

I'm glad to say everything was very soon turned on.

How near to disaster we heroes of the Resistance live in this world of cloak and dagger. I had planned to take a well-earned rest for a week or so – time to recuperate from my terrible experience at the château. But it was not to be. Scarcely had I removed The Fallen Madonna with the Big Boobies by Van Clomp from its resting place when the Gestapo arrived.

Even Edith's offer to sing privately to Otto Flick could not put him off. He had business to do, in the back room. And I knew that when he was finished with Helga, he would not be satisfied. It was a frightening thought.

I was trembling slightly as I showed Leclerc, the forger, the Madonna with the Big Boobies.

'Can you do another one?' I asked.

'You mean three Big Boobies?' the idiot replied, puzzled.

I made him aware of the gravity of the situation, but to no avail. He was prepared to attempt the artist's signature, but did not dare have a go at the boobies. I suppose he is rather old.

At that moment Maria announced that England was

calling on the radio concealed by Michelle of the
Resistance in the bedroom of my wife's mother. I doubted
that things could get worse, unless somebody lit a candle
without first opening the window. The old bat eats nothing
but onion soup.

The British airmen have been hiding in the cupboard
by her bed, so although I cannot understand a word they
say I expect they were as glad about the news from London
as I was. A plane was coming to pick them up a week
earlier than expected, and they had to leave immediately.
Michelle of the Resistance confirmed this when she
appeared like a phantom out of the night.

'Listen very carefully,' she said. 'I shall say this only
once. The airmen must leave immediately.'

I was characteristically decisive. 'They cannot leave
by the front; it is being watched. They cannot leave by the
back; Herr Flick is having dinner there.' They couldn't
leave by the window either, because the sheets from the
bed of my wife's mother which we tied together didn't
reach the ground.

Michelle was just quicker than me with the solution.
'They will have to leave disguised as Germans, in German
uniforms.'

War is hell. I only knew one way we could get hold of
them, especially at that time of night. 'I wouldn't ask this
of you normally,' I said to dear, sweet Yvette. 'But you will
be doing it for France!'

'I will be doing it for one hundred francs!' came the
reply.

'And Maria?'

'She will do it for seventy-five.'

I'm sorry to say that the Colonel wasn't so
accommodating. I explained that we only wanted to
borrow their uniforms for about fifteen minutes, and that
the airmen were taking the painting of The Fallen
Madonna with the Big Boobies to England to have it copied.
I mentioned that Yvette and Maria would be entertaining
him and the Captain in the meantime with the flying
helmet and the wet celery. I threw in the egg-whisk for

good measure and Berlin suddenly seemed to them to be very far away.*

10 FEBRUARY

I woke up this morning to the news that the Colonel was not pleased with me, and was going to have me shot. Or he would have done if his gun hadn't been in its holster which was attached to a British airman who was escaping in his uniform. I was the first to hear this news because it was the Colonel who woke me up.

Still, I managed to look on the bright side. At least Lieutenant Gruber didn't wake me up. He admired my rings at the bar yesterday and showed me a little trinket of his own, a locket he wears round his neck. It had a picture inside.

'What beautiful, long, blonde hair,' I said.

'Yes, isn't it,' he sighed. 'Unfortunately he had to have it cut off when he joined the army.'

I can't help feeling he's not one of us.

The Colonel was even less pleased when I pushed him and the Captain into the cupboard in the bedroom of my wife's mother. What could I do? Herr Flick of the Gestapo was coming up the stairs and they had no clothes on. I told my wife's mother to say nothing to Herr Flick, if she knew what was good for her. She had obviously forgotten what was good for her, but then she is very old too.

'Good morning, Madam,' Flick said. 'I am sorry to put you to inconvenience, but there are certain things I wish to know.'

'There are two German officers in the wardrobe and

---

* *One can only suppose from this exchange that René knows that food is the way to the Colonel's heart. Yvette and Maria are probably being asked to whip something up in the upstairs restaurant. I remain curious about this entry, though, because my mother was never a good cook. I can only imagine she was just that bit better than Maria.*

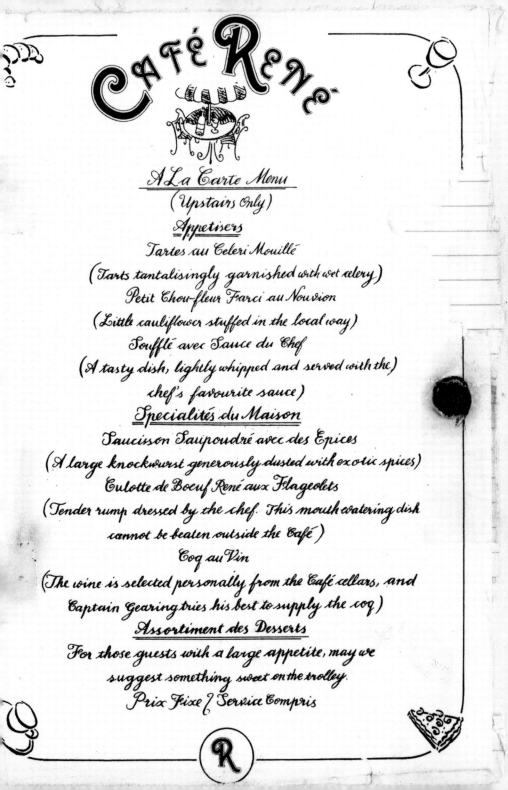

CAFÉ RENÉ

A La Carte Menu
(Upstairs Only)

Appetisers

Tartes au Celeri Mouillé

(Tarts tantalisingly garnished with wet celery)

Petit Chou-fleur Farci au Nouvion

(Little cauliflower stuffed in the local way)

Soufflé avec Sauce du Chef

(A tasty dish, lightly whipped and served with the)

chef's favourite sauce)

Specialités du Maison

Saucisson Saupoudré avec des Épices

(A large knockwurst generously dusted with exotic spices)

Culotte de Boeuf René aux Flageolets

(Tender rump dressed by the chef. This mouth watering dish

cannot be beaten outside the Café)

Coq au Vin

(The wine is selected personally from the Café cellars, and

Captain Gearing tries his best to supply the coq)

Assortiment des Desserts

For those guests with a large appetite, may we

suggest something sweet on the trolley.

Prix Fixe / Service Compris

the radio is under my bed,' the old bat blurted. And she has dared call me a coward.

'Very amusing,' Flick replied, 'I see I am wasting my time here. *Heil Hitler!*'

I admit I was sweating a bit when I went down to help Yvette and Maria with the chores. Yvette was desperate to

me, so I told her to go into the pantry and wait for me by the Brie. In the meantime I

Maria

and noticed that the velvet chaircover was showing signs of wear.*

Just then, Yvette returned to say there was no Brie and Michelle of the Resistance appeared with even worse news. The two British airmen had been captured by the Communist Resistance. So had the uniforms of the Colonel and the Captain being worn by the airmen. And so had The Fallen Madonna with the Big Boobies.

What were we to do? To get the Colonel and the Captain out of the wardrobe in the bedroom of my wife's mother, we had to get them uniforms. To get them uniforms, we had to contact London, where they could be made. To contact London, we had to use the radio in the bedroom of my wife's mother. I didn't think the Colonel and the Captain ought to know about the radio.

Unselfishly, I suggested that Michelle might be the person to sort things out. We agreed that the measurements for the uniforms would be sent to Savile Row by carrier pigeon. At midday, Maria would go to a secret address to pick up the pigeons. To avoid suspicion, she would be disguised as a small boy.

'Why can I not be disguised as a small girl?' she asked.

---

* *Another tantalising gap in the text. My mother must have gone to the pantry for a nibble, and was disappointed. But what of René and Maria? Was the bravest man in France schooling the young waitress in upholstery? He seems to think it was time to consider a little stuffing.*

'Because you are a small girl,' Michelle explained reasonably.

11 FEBRUARY

Michelle of the Resistance found the location of the captured British airmen and Leclerc found Fanny again. Fanny, I discover, is the name of my wife's mother. They were childhood sweethearts and would have married had he not gone to prison. Given the choice, I think I would have done the same.

I led the expedition to rescue the airmen. It was nothing, really. My fellow heroes and heroines of the Resistance said anyone could have done it.

The Fallen Madonna with the Big Boobies is now back in safe hands. I wish I could say the same for the German uniforms. The foolish airmen burnt them when the communists took flight because they thought they would be shot as spies.

I might not tell the Colonel and Captain about this turn of events until tomorrow.

12 FEBRUARY

Or tomorrow.

13 FEBRUARY

Or the next day.

> Hans's are red
> The Colonels are blue
> Goebbels hasn't got any
> How about you?

14 Février

14 FEBRUARY

Jour de St Valentine

Valentine's Day!
    I received just one card, unsigned, but perfumed with lily of the valley and a hint of diesel oil.
    I sent only two. Both carried the same message.

> My love is like a celery stick,
> Divided into two.
> My leaves I give to Edith,
> But the stalk I give to you.

15 FEBRUARY

For the last few days Colonel Von Strohm and Captain Geering have been lurking in the café dressed as onion-sellers. These disguises were left in the wardrobe in the bedroom of my wife's mother by the escaping British airmen. And it is not even the onion season.

'Ah, Pierre, Jacques – the onion-sellers,' I greeted them as they sidled into the restaurant. 'Wine for my friends Pierre and Jacques. Sit down here, my friends.' Then, in a whisper, 'A brilliant disguise, my friends. We will get your uniforms as quickly as possible.'

'You said that yesterday, René,' said the Colonel.

'And the day before, and the day before that,' piped the Captain.

'If we don't get them today, you will be shot,' said the Colonel.

'Up against the wall, with guns,' piped the Captain.

I could tell that they weren't impressed, although even as these harsh threats were uttered I saw tears of compassion in their eyes.

'It is these damned onions,' said the Colonel, but he didn't fool me.

I moved to attend to my other customers as Maria came in with the basket of carrier pigeons, dressed as a small boy.* Thinking quickly, I welcomed her. 'Aha, little Georges, my nephew. It is good to see you, lad.'

'I have got what you want, Uncle,' she said, and I couldn't help noticing she had. Lieutenant Gruber, who was in his favourite position at the bar, noticed too.

'That boy is very well built, René,' he said with approval.

'Ah, it is my wife's cooking.'

'Why is he wearing stockings and suspenders?'

'We have many problems with him.'

---

* *This remains obscure. Why were the carrier pigeons dressed as a small boy?*

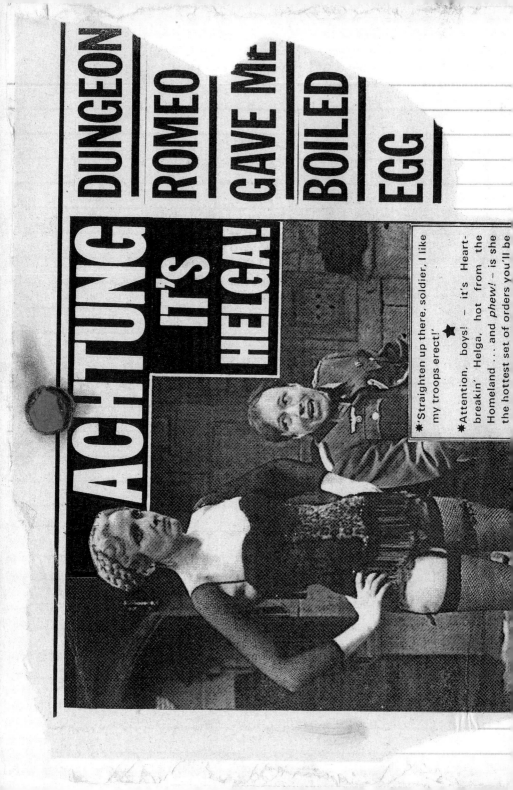

DUNGEON ROMEO GAVE ME BOILED EGG

ACHTUNG IT'S HELGA!

* Straighten up there, soldier, I like my troops erect!'

* Attention, boys! – it's Heart-breakin' Helga, hot from the Homeland … and *phew!* – is she the hottest set of orders you'll be

...right now I am under the Colonel at the château ...' barks our Heavenly High-heeled Hip-hugger (36–24–36) – and rumour has it there's certainly a lot of lucky privates on parade up there!

★ But not to worry, boys – action-hungry Helga says she's gother eye on the Tank Corps for a posting soon ....

★ Corps blimey, that's what we say! She can come and play with our helmets anytime!!

DER SUN SAYS:

STICK IT UP YOUR JUNKERS

LE CAFE RENÉ

"Home of Café René – the finest Café in all France" proclaims the sign at the entrance to the quiet Normandy village of Nouvion, in the same quaint, rustic lettering that characterises Der Menu Touristisch in the Café window.

From the outside, the Café looks unremarkable enough, standing in the village square opposite the butcher with the big chopper. But is it indeed the finest Café in all France? Does *le patron*, René Artois, really deserve to be hailed – as he was by one recent anonymous contributor to this guide – as one of the great new stars of French cuisine and entertainment?

Certainly the menu is inventive, based on what Artois is determined to call his 'navel cuisine'. He prides himself, as chef, on his tasty tit bits. "The big hunk of meat is a thing of the past," he says, "unless the guest wishes to enjoy the delights of the more private dining room upstairs. There he will be able to enjoy everything from a little nibble to a grande bouffe in the French style."

It is in the philosophy of M. Le Patron as well as the dishes themselves that the true genius of Artois' creativity is displayed. Two contented diners, resplendent in their field grey uniforms, assured us that the waitresses are certainly generous with their portions, and though the service charge may appear a little steep, customers very seldom lost their shirts.

Wines have had to be decanted out of their bottles owing, in the words of Artois, to "agitation during a bombing raid." In the course of decanting they seem to have become a little on the thin side for the taste of our inspectors, but this is perhaps just a reflection of the choice of vintage. Artois also has his own-label cognacs, though these, too, seem to be from the same cru.

Artois himself cuts a noble figure as he walks around the Café in his white apron, chatting aimiably to customers. He is very much in the modern idiom of the working class hero, a man almost humbled by his own talent, resisting the lures of fame in favour of staying firmly in the saddle in Nouvion. René Artois is not a man to swan around opening supermarkets when he can be doing what he does best, inspecting the firmness of the melons in the larder, or kneading some dumplings in the kitchen.

Complaints from our correspondents are few, but one or two otherwise satisfied habitues of the Café would have welcomed a more extensive selection from the cheese board on cabaret nights.

I was wondering how the conversation was going to develop when Helga arrived with Herr Flick. The Gestapo officer went unerringly to the table of the Colonel and the Captain who were disguised as onion-sellers.

Herr Flick did not beat about the bush. 'Why are you dressed in the fashion of onion-sellers?'

'We can explain,' said the Colonel.

'He can explain,' piped the Captain.

'I am trying to infiltrate the Resistance,' said the Colonel. 'Dressed as a Colonel the French avoid me. With these I am one of them.'

At this Lieutenant Gruber forgot about the small boy with the stockings and suspenders. 'I am one of them too,' he said cheerfully.

After Herr Flick left to show Helga his private quarters, the Colonel returned to the subject of the uniforms. I tried to soothe him with the news that they were being made in London, by the finest tailors in Savile Row, but for some reason he became even angrier and decided that he was definitely going to hand me over to the Gestapo who would have me shot.

Once again I stared disaster in the face. There was only one thing for it. I reminded him that he had helped the British airmen to escape. I reminded him that he had stolen the priceless painting of The Fallen Madonna.

'René,' he said, 'I'm not sure you realise it, but this war is getting very dangerous.'

I reminded him of the flying helmet and the wet celery. That seemed to do the trick.

16 FEBRUARY

The airmen are back.

I had told Edith to do something unforgettable for the Colonel's lunch and was half-way through disciplining Maria about her stockings and suspenders when they appeared dressed as scarecrows at the back window. I

Duet for René and Edith

Composed by Roger and Leclerc

EDITH:
Outfits from Paris and nylons from Britain;
Letters from Alphonse that show how he's smitten;
Randy old suitors who want their last fling,
These are a few of my favourite things...

EDITH:
Boys in grey tunics with red shoulder flashes:
Chaps who own cafes with sexy moustaches;
Men who adore every note that I sing,
These are a few of my favourite things...

RENE:
Big balls of Edam and fingers of Gouda;
Soft runny goat's ones and some even ruder;
All kinds of cheese and the peace that it brings,
These are a few of my favourite things...

RENE:
When Leclerc plays,
When my wife sings,
When I'm feeling grim;
I simply remember my favourite cheese,
And then I don't hear a thing.

...dents are fe...
...e or two otherwis...
...fied habitues of the
...afé would have wel-
comed a more extensive
selection   from   the
cheese   board   on
cabaret nights.

...d
...ured
...resses

don't know what they do for the crows but they scare the living daylights out of me. I have a terrible feeling that we are not going to get rid of these lunatics easily.

17 FEBRUARY

We communicated wih London today, which is just as well since Edith casseroled the carrier pigeons for the Colonel's lunch. I was pleased to be able to tell our onion-sellers that their uniforms were being made by Solomon and Klein, the very finest tailors on Savile Row, and that they would be delivered by the RAF at dawn tomorrow.

The news wasn't greeted with quite the enthusiasm I anticipated. The Colonel was rather upset about the idea of wearing a Wehrmacht uniform with a Solomon and Klein label and the Captain was rather upset that he hadn't had the opportunity to order some extra shirts.

Edith was threatening to sing another song to tide us over this slightly difficult moment when Helga and Herr Flick entered the café, dressed as onion-sellers. I gathered from Helga later that the Gestapo officer had been very much impressed by the Colonel's plan to infiltrate the Resistance.

This he told her during a short period of casual interrogation yesterday afternooon. She seems to spend a lot of time in Herr Flick's soundproofed dungeon these days. Perhaps she is looking for ways of curing his limp
a big softie*

and actually the soundproofing is to stop him being disturbed at night by the sound of heavy lorries.

---

* *I cannot be sure if Himmler himself censored this fascinating glimpse of a Gestapo officer on the job, or whether these two lines went the same route as the other missing parts of the diary.*

Interestingly enough, my mother says she never realised that Otto Flick had a limp. She just assumed it was the way he walked.

That's as maybe. As far as I'm concerned the Gestapo is the Gestapo is the Gestapo, especially when it calls Heinrich Himmler 'Uncle'. And even more especially when it has vowed to track down the hero of the Resistance who is hiding the painting of The Fallen Madonna with the Big Boobies by Van Clomp and have him shot.

Talking of which, I shall be very relieved when the RAF fly in at dawn tomorrow morning because they will be taking that too.

18 FEBRUARY

It is 3.00 am and I cannot sleep. It is often the case when we heroes of the Resistance are on the brink of action. I thought about arousing Maria and discussing my position by the icebox. Then I thought about discussing it in the cellar instead.

'But René,' I remember her saying to me once (or possibly twice), 'I get so dirty in there.'

She was right. And it is 3.00 am. I'm not sure I have the strength.

So here I am, dear Diary, to record the dramatic juggling act that I was called upon to perform yesterday evening. It is so difficult these days to keep all the Bols in

Yvette, Edith and Lt Gruber discuss René's bols

the air, especially when two of them are yours, and another is a bottle full of nitro-glycerine.

Let me explain.

I was in the process of asking Yvette to work with me under cover at around eleven o'clock tonight when Michelle of the Resistance appeared like a phantom out of the late afternoon.

'Now listen very carefully,' she said. 'I shall say this only once. You are to take this container and hide it in your cellar.'

'What does the container contain?' I asked.

'Bols,' she replied, brusquely.

I'm not easily offended, but I was a bit upset by her attitude, particularly since I have put myself between her and the enemy on so many occasions.

'No, no,' she said only once, unwrapping a bottle. 'Bols gin. This type of gin is coloured a very pale blue. Nitro-glycerine is also coloured a very pale blue. Be extremely gentle with it. Hide it in your cellar. At eleven o'clock there is going to be a big bang.'

I had to admit that her intelligence was impressive. 'I don't know what you are talking about,' I said.

'I will return quite soon to collect it. It is to blow up the railway line.'

All in all, it turned out to be a very explosive evening. Lieutenant Gruber spotted the bottle immediately, before I had a chance to put it in the cellar. He told me he was in the mood for something a little different. I thought about suggesting a girl, but he insisted on a Bols. I said that I didn't want to open a new bottle just to serve one drink.

'Very well, René,' he smiled that smile again, 'Two Bols. And perhaps you would like to give your wife one?'

This is obviously developing into a very popular German joke. 'Out of the question,' I said. But I still failed to avert catastrophe. Edith gave her mother a couple of glasses, and she blew the door off the cupboard in her room where the two British airmen are hiding again. They are having a terrible war. Even worse, Maria mixed some Bols with the chicken-feed to make them lay better. She said it always worked for her.

I'm sad to say that the poor things are now only good for stuffing pillows.

20 MARCH

Well, it has happened. Even the bravest man in France is not immortal. I know everybody warned me that it was on the cards, but it still took me by surprise. And what's more, it hurt. *Mon Dieu*, how it hurt!

I have been shot and killed.

And I'm too upset about it to write any more today.

21 MARCH

I must again plead your forgivenesss.* To recount to you the full, tragic story of the events leading up to my death may take many days, despite the fact that Yvette said yesterday evening that she would take dictation. I reluctantly declined her offer. Although her speed is as impressive as it ever was, my knees are still shaking.

22 MARCH

Forgive me, dear Diary. I'm still in a bit of a state. I have just been measured for my coffin by Monsieur Alfonse the undertaker, and my wife has chosen the most expensive oak casket with brass handles.

I may have recovered by tomorrow, but I doubt it.

---

* *It is typical of the author that although he had never intended this diary for publication, he maintains the most courteous and balanced tone towards his reader, even at a time of great personal distress.*

Today I am, after all, feeling a little calmer. To explain –
as we made our way through the early dawn to rendezvous
with the plane that was going to deliver the uniforms of
the Colonel and the Captain and pick up the two British
airmen and the one painting of The Fallen Madonna with
the two boobies (Leclerc never did get his hands on it) I
thought everything was going to be simple.

How wrong can one be?

This nightmare began over a month ago now, but it's
as if it were yesterday. Death plays strange tricks on a
man's memory.

There were apparently some things that Helga had not
revealed to us, though the Captain says not many. She
chose the night of the long Bols to reveal one that had
grave implications for every hero of the Resistance, and
especially me. General Von Klinkerhoffen was arriving at
ten o'clock the next morning for a thorough inspection of
all personnel.

It has to be said that the Colonel and the Captain were
not that pleased about it either. They were still dressed as
onion-sellers and their spare uniforms were in Berlin at
the de luxe cleaners. That is why they decided to join us.

When the Tiger Moth landed, everyone except the
British airmen noticed two things. The first was that it
was a Tiger Moth and therefore had only two seats,
including the pilot's. The second was that the Jewish tailor
who travelled as passenger had only been booked for one
appointment. He was happy to oblige with a fitting, but
was unwilling for some reason to stay with us until he had
finished the uniforms. As a result there was only room in
the plane when it left for The Fallen Madonna with the Big
Boobies, and even she took a bit of a squeeze.

I remained philosophical. The airmen were still with
us, and the Colonel and the Captain would get nice new
uniforms when General Von Klinkerhoffen sent them to
the Russian Front, except that they probably wouldn't

have Solomon and Klein labels. I resolved to return to *Le Café René* and make the best of things.

I hadn't realised that Michelle of the Resistance had immediate need of my heroism.

'Now listen very carefully,' she said before I had gone three paces. 'These are the orders for our next move. From here we go north.'

I've had more profitable orders. 'If you don't mind my saying, my café is south,' I explained patiently.

'The railway is north.'

'But we could walk home,' I said helpfully. 'Why take a train?'

'First we have to blow up the railway.'

That is when my real troubles began.

24 MARCH

'Hans,' the Colonel said to the Captain as the Tiger Moth disappeared into the distance, 'we are German officers. We are part of the great army that is winning the war. We do not blow up our own supply lines.'

'On the other hand,' the Captain piped, 'if we help them blow up the railway Von Klinkerhoffen's train will not arrive so we won't have to meet it so we won't need our uniforms so he won't find out we haven't got them.'

'And if you don't co-operate we will shoot you and hide your corpses in the copse.' I think it's fair to say that Michelle had the last word on the subject.

I led the heroic little band as it made its way gingerly through the undergrowth. I wasn't actually at the front, though, preferring instead to adopt a neat manœuvre

Lieutenant Gruber once told me he learnt at the Academy which involved leading from the back.*

It seemed to work very well, except that I was closer to Yvette than I felt comfortable with. Every now and then a glimpse of her thigh reminded me that she had something very explosive concealed beneath her skirt. I suspect that she was as relieved as we all were to be able to unstrap the bottle of nitro-glycerine from her leg when we reached the cutting.

Michelle of the Resistance was worried that we might not have enough Bols to blow up the railway line, but the Captain proved that he had by throwing it by accident onto the track. I must say this surprised me. He's only a little fellow, and very short-sighted. I made a mental note to take this up with Maria.

I think it was then that the knockwurst really hit the fan. There was a huge explosion, and suddenly there were German soldiers everywhere. I fought bravely, as you would expect, but we were quickly overwhelmed. Surrender, alas, was the only answer.

As we were frogmarched to the cells, I thought not of myself. I thought of Edith wending her way sadly to the room of her mother with the news of my capture. And I thought of the smile on the old bat's face as she would say: 'You should have married the butcher. He like you. Every time you pass his shop he wave at you with his chopper.'

---

* *I initially assumed this to refer to the famed Military Academy at Heidelberg, but research has shown that the name of Hubert Gruber appeared only on the roll of the Dance Academy in Cologne.*

As we languished in the cells, even the Colonel reckoned the situation was serious, and he was the only person who could order our release. However, he could only do so by signing the papers in his office, and to do that he had to escape.

Helga thoughtfully provided a hacksaw to cut through the bars of the small window set high in the prison wall, and not so thoughtfully told us that General Von Klinkerhoffen was shortly to arrive by car. Apparently he was none too pleased about the railway track.

Since the Colonel could not fit through the small window, bars or no bars, I offered to try. This was not viewed favourably. I got the strong impression that if push came to shove the Colonel would tell the General that he thought the Captain might know something about the explosion. And the Captain would mention me.

I had a sudden image of them being taken away to Gestapo HQ for questioning, still carrying their onions. would cause quite a stink in Berlin. It was causing quite a stink where we were.

Yvette, of course, was a tower of strength. Maria, when she visited us to deliver another hacksaw blade, was the same, only smaller. They both wanted so much to place their bodies by my side if we were to be shot. I told them bravely that I'd rather they placed them in front, but there is a time and a place for everything.

Leclerc, the forger, came to pay his respects, disguised with his usual flair as a priest. He also delivered a hacksaw blade, along with the news that my wife and mother-in-law were coming to see me. Things were clearly going to get worse.

I thought the Captain had it bad; he now had three hacksaw blades hidden down his trousers. I would have taken them myself if I'd realised that no sooner were our visitors to appear than the Colonel and the Captain would escape, dressed in their clothes. It is the only time I have seen the Colonel grateful for his uncanny resemblance to my wife's mother.

Incarcerated then with those two women, death suddenly lost some of its sting. And when Edith told me she would sing the Marseillaise as the firing squad took aim, I hoped they would be quick on the trigger.

I must stop now. The very thought of Edith singing the Marseillaise drives me to the cognac bottle.

26 MARCH

I shall never forget being brought before General Von Klinkerhoffen in chains. The Germans obviously feared greatly that I was thinking of escaping to the hills, there to rally the forces of the Maquis behind me. They weren't far wrong.

The Colonel, to do him justice, said I should be released. He may have had The Fallen Madonna with the Big Boobies on his mind.

'I do not agree,' the General replied. 'We will shoot him as an example, tomorrow at dawn. Colonel, how does seven o'clock suit you?'

'Later would be better for me,' I said, even with Edith singing the Marseillaise. But it was not to be.

I faced the firing squad as the sun came up and bathed Lieutenant Gruber in its rosy glow. When he came closer

I realised he was wearing blusher. He was to command the squad.

'This is a very sad occasion for me, René.'

'I feel the same way, Lieutenant.'

'You French are so brave. Your mother-in-law has not one single tear.'

'This I believe,' I said. 'What about my wife?'

'She says she is going to sing the Marseillaise. Do you wish a blindfold?'

Earplugs would be better, I reflected. I could see Yvette and Maria in the distance, tears cascading down their cheeks. They must also have known what Edith had in store.

The squad raised their guns, took aim and fired. It was mercifully all over. Today was my funeral. It also went with a bang. Michelle of the Resistance had hidden some landmines in my coffin and it hit a tree.

Yvette and Maria cling to fond memories of René as they escort his coffin to its final resting place

I should perhaps mention at this stage that the Colonel and the Captain had given the firing squad wooden bullets, which disintegrate three metres in front of the rifle. So I am not really dead, of course, though it still jolly well hurt. Only now I am managing to remove the last of the splinters with Yvette lending a hand.

The whole experience has had a very undesirable effect on me. Lieutenant Gruber has been kind enough to deny this, and so of course have Yvette and Maria. But I'm not the man I once was. The fact is, I have become my identical twin brother René, recently arrived from Nancy to run the café.

It was the Colonel's idea, and it seems to have worked. Herr Flick swallowed the story when Helga told him.

'After some interrogation,' she added.

The Colonel blanched. 'Why did he interrogate you?'

'It was raining, so we decided not to go out.'

With Lieutenant Gruber it was not so easy, but then it never is. And he was in charge of the firing squad.

'I hope you won't hold it against me,' he said.

I assured him I wouldn't.

'You bear a most remarkably close resemblance to your late brother. You even have the same pretty rings. But now I come to look, your eyelashes are a little longer and your hands seem more artistic.'

It was a very bad sign, now that I was a single man, and from Nancy into the bargain.

Otherwise little has changed. The two British airmen have moved from the bedroom of my wife's mother to the henhouse, where they are probably disguised as turkeys. Roger Leclerc has moved from the cellar to the bed of my wife's mother, where he is disguised as a complete idiot. They are all very convincing disguises. I wish I felt better about my own.

Today it was the Colonel's birthday. He wouldn't say
which, though Yvette tells me he is in some ways still
remarkably youthful. I baked him a cake. The icing was
plaster of Paris because the Captain failed to supply the
sugar, but the candles were real.

'In France,' I told him, 'it is the tradition that they
must be blown out by one big puff.'

'It is your birthday, Colonel,' Lieutenant Gruber said
generously.

Yvette had a surprise for him in her bedroom at nine
o'clock this evening. Maria had a surprise for him at eight.
All in all it made me rather look forward to my next
birthday. Until Edith announced that she would surprise
him too, with a special song.

'Your wife has many talents, René,' piped the Captain
when Edith had finished.

'A pity they do not include singing,' the Colonel said.
I had to agree. Edith could not carry a tune in a bucket.

'A little champagne, Colonel,' I said. After my ordeal,
I was in an expansive mood.

'With champagne glasses!' He was delighted to see
what Maria was carrying.

'Of course. And I will tell you a legend. It is said that
these glasses were modelled on the bosom of Marie An-
toinette.'

'They should have been modelled on Helga's bosom,'
piped the Captain, 'we'd have got a bigger drink.'

'There is also a legend about where they got the idea
for the champagne cork,' Lieutenant Gruber said.

'Let us talk no longer of the past.' The Colonel spoke
for all of us. 'Let there be wine, women –'

'And song!' Edith cried joyously.

'No!' said the Colonel. 'Just wine and women.'

It is really very sad that just as they were starting to
enjoy themselves, the Captain and the Colonel were seized
by the girls of the Communist Resistance and taken away

How can one do justice to the memory of the man who for so many in the heroic Allied forces came in his short life to symbolise all that was good and profitable in these troubled times?

Rene Artois, killed tragically in action, will undoubtedly be in line for the highest award for gallantry it is in His Majesty's power to bestow.

He is survived by his widow, Edith, and is mourned by his many friends.

Colonel Artois (though he was too modest to use his rank) spent much of the war undercover, but his exploits have become legendary. Attractive, courageous, vita

THE TIMES

How can one do justice to the memory of the man who for so many heroes of the Wehrmacht (and the SS) came in his short life to symbolise all that was good and profitable in these troubled times?

Rene Artois, executed as a result of a tragic administrative blunder, should undoubtedly be in line for the highest award for gallantry it is in the Führer's power to bestow.

He is survived by his widow, Edith, and is mourned by his many friends in the Wehrmacht (and the SS).

Rene Artois spent much of the war undercover, looking for the Fallen Madonna with the Big Boobies by Van Klomp, which he always meant to give the Führer for his birthday. He

DIE WELT

How can one do justice to the memory of the man who for so many heroes of the Resistance came in his short life to symbolise all that was good and profitable in these troubled times?

Rene Artois, killed tragically in action, will undoubtedly be in line for the highest award for gallantry it is in General De Gaulle's power to bestow.

He is survived by his widow, Edith, and is mourned by his many friends.

Colonel Artois (though he was too modest to use his rank) spent much of the war undercover, but his exploits have become legendary. Attractive, courageous, vital, he

FRANCE SOIR

Even in the midst of war the national and international press were quick to print eulogies of the man who for so many had come to symbolise all that was good and profitable in these difficult times.

The unenviable task of summing up the many virtues and achievements in the life of Rene Artois fell, not surprisingly, to his twin brother, Rene Artois.

to be shot. Their crime? Ordering my own execution only a few short days before.

I must admit that the irony was not lost on me. Nor was the fact that I might not have to share the painting of The Fallen Madonna with the Big Boobies by Van Clomp. Call me a hero, call me a sentimental fool, but I have always felt strongly that they should remain in the hands of a Frenchman.

29 MARCH

I couldn't sleep a wink last night. Yvette and Maria were almost inconsolable, and naturally, because they served under me, I had to attend to them. Yvette, as always, was worried that her poor, crippled mother would not survive without the food parcels and paraffin she had persuaded the Colonel to supply.* Maria was just worried that her own appetite would not be satisfied, and I must say this morning so am I.

Breakfast was a sorry affair. We were all extremely upset that there was no butter, very little sugar, and only one cup of coffee that I felt compelled to drink personally to keep morale up. I began to realise that we might have to rescue these Germans, for the good of France.

---

* *It is a great tribute to my mother's self-sacrifice that my maternal grandmother lived to the age of 103, and was by all accounts entertaining her friends in a very energetic fashion right up to her death.*

30 MARCH

Michelle of the Resistance appeared this evening, like a phantom out of the wardrobe in the back room. It is less than two days since the Colonel and the Captain were kidnapped, but already their absence has been noticed. Herr Flick was on his way to the café at that very moment.

'Listen very carefully, I shall say this only once,' she said. 'The Gestapo will investigate the disappearance of the Colonel and if they find the transmitter and the codebook you will all have had your chips.'

We acted with characteristic speed. Michelle threw the radio out of the window of the room of my wife's mother onto a passing truck whilst I fed the book page by page to the two British airmen. I think they would have preferred to eat something hot, but they had to make do with code.

Flick interrogated us all closely, and it wasn't as much fun as Helga keeps implying. Lieutenant Gruber was especially worried that the Gestapo would discover that he was bending over behind the bar at the time of the abduction.

'You!' Flick barked. 'Did you see the face of the kidnapper?'

'She was just an ordinary French girl,' Gruber replied uncomfortably.

'Would you recognise her?'

'All girls look the same to me.'

Flick responded by telling him to round up ten peasants and shoot them in the town square if the Colonel and the Captain were not found. That decided me. That, and the fact that I hadn't even had a cup of coffee for breakfast that morning.

31 MARCH

I would have gone alone, but in the event two girls from the Communist Resistance pounced on me late last night when I was putting the cat out. I assumed they were acquainted with my reputation, but they were only there to escort me to the lonely barn where the Colonel and the Captain were imprisoned. I was glad of their company, particularly since I was blindfolded.

'You are the brother of the man who was shot,' the leader of the band told me when I arrived. 'You are to have the honour of shooting the men who have raped France.'

It is true that these men were our enemies, though I felt the use of the word 'rape' was a little strong. Maria for one had always seemed most obliging. How was I to explain to these courageous but naive women that for René Artois things were not so straightforward? Their war was a series of small-scale raids, whilst I was in control of the big picture. Or would be as soon as the RAF delivered it.

Although every fibre of my being cried out against it, I resolved to deceive them. 'I would like to savour the moment of revenge alone.'

I had just had time to chastise the Colonel for getting us into this mess when the Resistance band returned. They had intercepted an RAF parachute drop whose contents they found baffling: two German uniforms tailored in Savile Row and two identical paintings by Van Clomp. They dropped everything when shots were suddenly fired outside. They must have been very frightened.

Our rescuers were Michelle, Yvette, Maria and Edith,

dressed in German uniforms. My wife was wearing the jackboots, but the mission was Michelle's idea. There is clearly no limit to her desire to have me as leader of our heroic group.

We greeted each other with fond embraces, as is the French custom, and I shook hands warmly with Edith before making my way back to the café.

I was just putting the finishing touches to this entry and Yvette was complimenting me on my style when we were aroused by banging downstairs. The Colonel and the Captain had come to deliver the painting of the Fallen Madonna, and the news that Herr Flick was in possession of the forgery.

1 APRIL

April Fool's Day – but when I told the Colonel and the Captain early this morning that they had given the original to Herr Flick and kept the forgery by mistake, I wasn't joking.

When they said that unless I got the real one back before it was sent to the Fuhrer in Berlin I would be shot, they weren't either.

I felt at last that everything was returning to normal.

2 APRIL

Maria and I were in the pantry having a little nibble at the Brie when Michelle of the Resistance called to tell me that the new radio transmitter was being delivered today by that old fool Leclerc, disguised as a cheese salesman.

'He will be the bearer of a suitcase containing cheese,' she said only once.

'How will he carry the radio?' I asked.

'He has a false bottom.'

I wondered why in that case he needed the suitcase. I

also wondered what we would do with the extra cheese. The only answer was to ask Edith to do a special Gala Cabaret Night.

I'm afraid that I only have the strength for a short entry today because my wife interrupted a bout of hand-to-hand combat I was having with Yvette in the back room. The only way of convincing her that I was teaching our waitresses self-defence was by asking Yvette to demonstrate on me how she would fight off the drunken overtures of a German soldier. Unfortunately, she did.

3 APRIL

Bad news from the Colonel, especially for a man with a hernia. Herr Flick of the Gestapo is putting the painting of the Fallen Madonna with the Big Boobies on the train to Berlin tomorrow at mid-day. Hitler has told Himmler to pick it up personally.

'Here is what we do, René,' he said. 'By my orders tonight you will close your café for my private party to celebrate the anniversary of the burning down of the Reichstag. Helga here will give Herr Flick information about the party and tell him that he is not invited.'

'I only have to hint and he will drag it out of me,' she said.

'This will arouse his suspicions and he will not be able to stay away. While Herr Flick is enjoying himself with the girls dressed as Hitler Youths, you will be at his private quarters switching the paintings.'

Somehow I knew there was going to be a catch. I wanted nothing to do with Herr Flick's private quarters. It was very dangerous to mess with the Gestapo.

With my usual generosity, I offered to give the party instead.

Just then that old fool Leclerc delivered the new radio concealed in a Dutch Edam. It was never my favourite cheese, and went down further in my estimation when it crackled into life whilst I still had it behind the bar.

'Listen carefully,' it said, 'I will meet you behind the woodshed at one o'clock.'

I later discovered from the new code book that I was being told to take the two British airmen to the coast tonight. Unfortunately Lieutenant Gruber got the impression that I was inviting him to share some intimate memories of my boyhood in Nancy.

'See you later then,' he said gaily.

It was turning into quite an evening.

I left the party before it had even started. Lieutenant Gruber was at the piano, singing *Falling in Love Again*. It never fails to bring tears to my eyes, and certainly didn't then.

We made our way courageously to the château. I was dressed in the Savile Row uniform of the Colonel and Edith was in the Captain's, but again she wore the jackboots.

I regret now that I was generous enough to let her take charge. I feel sure that if the pillow with which I was bulking out the uniform of the Colonel had not started to slip towards my crutch, I would not be in the position I am now – back at the café having left the copy of the painting of the Fallen Madonna with the Big Boobies in Herr Flick's room, and without repossessing the original.

And what Lieutenant Gruber is going to make of the pillow when I get to the woodshed I dread to think.

4 APRIL

I backed out of our meeting in the woodshed. It seemed the only way. Lieutenant Gruber was upset, of course, but consoled himself with a little pirouette or two on the dance floor.

The party was a great success, judging by the state of the restaurant this morning. The only shorts left behind the bar belonged to the girls dressed in the uniform of the Hitler Youth.

Taking the two British airmen to the beach to pick up their boat home was not so much fun. It wasn't until we got there that Michelle discovered that one of them got seasick even on the boating lake of Regent's Park.*

As we headed back to the café with them, I wasn't pleased. I had led our brave little group through the coastal defences at great personal risk. We had disguised ourselves by then as Hitler Youths, and my trousers were very tight.

Yvette, at least, was as supportive as always. 'René, I feel tonight that the years have fallen away from you,' she said. 'You sound much younger too.'

I was doubly glad that Lieutenant Gruber was not waiting in the woodshed.

12 APRIL

It has been more than a week since I put pen to paper. This is because it has been a very slow week for business. I've needed both hands, as well as the help of my staff, to massage some feeling back into my lower limbs. With uniforms that tight, I'm amazed the Hitler Youth haven't lost more of their members.

The British airmen have been hidden in the nearby nunnery. For a while I thought it might be all I was good for as well.

I discovered this morning that Herr Flick also had made a forgery of the painting of the Fallen Madonna with the Big Boobies by Van Clomp. He now has not two but six boobies in his hands. And that's not including Helga.

* This sounds very much like my stepfather.

13 APRIL

There has been a lot of banging here recently, but it is only my demented widow in the back room looking for my will, which leaves everything I possess to her.

She can bang all day. It is hidden in a compartment behind the cuckoo clock where she will never find it.

14 APRIL

She has found it.

I was taking a drink rather gingerly with Lieutenant Gruber when the cuckoo gave a strangled cry and my secret was out.

' "I do hereby leave all of which I stand possessed," ' Edith read triumphantly, ' "to my dear and faithful wife, who has comforted me and filled me with joy during the happy days of my marriage." '

'The nights were a different story,' I muttered.

'There is something written on the back,' Yvette said.

' "P.S. To Yvette . . ." ' Edith read. 'I can hardly read it. It is as if his hands were shaking.'

'He must have been getting on a bit by then,' I said.

'No, I've got it. "To Yvette, who has served so devotedly under me, I leave the collapsible sofa in the parlour." ' Edith's brow furrowed. 'That sofa is not collapsible.'

'It is unless you put a book under it,' Yvette said

brightly.

' "P.P.S.," ' Edith continued. ' "To Maria, I leave the small billiard table which has given us both so many moments of pleasure." '

I have to admit that I've had some lucky breaks on that table.

'Dear René,' Lieutenant Gruber said wistfully. 'He was a good man. There was something soft and sensitive about him.'

'I know how he felt,' I said.

15 APRIL

Since my death, life has not been bleaker. For a whole day now my widow has been helping herself to my estate. My best cognac, the cash out of the till, all the things a Frenchman holds sacred are now technically hers.

Well, not quite all. I must admit that I am gaining considerable pleasure from the fact that both Yvette and Maria are already putting my bequests to them to immediate good use.*

---

* I can confirm everything the great man says. The collapsible sofa still has pride of place in our parlour all these years later. I often return from the office to discover my mother putting her feet up on it.

As for the billiard table, she tells me that Maria left it behind when she mailed herself to Switzerland, but not before considerably improving her technique.

Odes to a Nancy Boy

War Poem

If I should cry, think only this of me.
That there was some corner of the Russian
front

That was very, very cold...

Ode to Rene's own Label Cognacs

They shall not grow old, as we
that are left grow old
Age shall not weary them, nor the
years condemn.
As the going down of the bottle and into
the morning
We will remember them, even if you
forget where you put the label.

16 APRIL

I'm under a great deal of pressure.

My widow is spending all my money attempting to attract a new suitor. She is parading herself around Nouvion in a new hat which looks like a dead hen, trying to lure a rival café-owner into her grasp. The mother of my widow rubs salt into my wounds by adding that he has a bigger one than me. That's definitely the last time I wear the uniform of the Hitler Youth.

The Colonel is being equally harsh. He is threatening to have me shot again unless I give him the names of my Resistance group.

'But Colonel,' I say courageously, 'I do not know their names. They are mostly girls, and only reveal themselves at night.'

'I wish to get my hands on them,' said the Colonel.

'Me too,' piped the Captain.

It took all my powers of inventiveness to divert their line of questioning, and quite a lot of wet celery.

'And the flying helmet,' said the Colonel.

'And the flying helmet,' I agreed.*

'And a great big steaming plate of spaghetti bolognese and three feet of elastic,' piped the Captain.

We were both speechless for a moment.

'Hans,' said the Colonel slowly, 'Just between the two of us, what exactly have you got in mind?'

'I thought I would have a quick snack while Maria repairs my long winter underwear.'

17 APRIL

Hubert Gruber and I are getting to know each other much better these days. I'm not convinced it is a good idea, but it is for France.

He told me today that Herr Flick had a compromising

---

* *There are many references to the flying helmet throughout the text. I can only assume that the Colonel was preparing to perform some fairly complex aerobatic manœuvres.*

photograph of him and, worst of all, with a woman. 'My commanding officer will never forgive me, René,' he said, 'and I'm most concerned that this will change *our* relationship.'

I assured him it wouldn't.

Apparently Flick will reveal the photograph if Hubert tells anybody about his recent glimpse of the Gestapo officer's private quarters.

'Flick has three Fallen Madonnas with Big Boobies, René. One is a forgery he commissioned himself, one arrived mysteriously at his HQ, and one is genuine. A peasant was clearing his room and mixed them up.'

'How do you know all this?' I said, feigning disinterest.

'I was taken there in a sack.'

'How dreadful,' I said.

'Actually, I found it rather exciting. The soldier who carried the sack had very broad shoulders.'

'But why?'

'I expect he takes a lot of exercise.'

'No,' I said. 'Why did Herr Flick want to see you?'

'He knew I had artistic leanings.'

'But I thought he was interrogating Helga pretty much full time these days,' I said, baffled.

'Yes,' Hubert replied. 'He only wanted me to tell him which was the real painting. I was able to identify one as a genuine early Van Clomp.'

I asked him how.

'When he was taller he signed his paintings further up.'

18 APRIL

The Colonel was very anxious about Lieutenant Gruber's visit to Gestapo HQ. He interrupted me during a special service I was holding for myself in the back room. It was the only way I could account for the presence of the two British airmen, who have returned dressed as nuns, though I did think of saying we were collecting for my organ fund.

'René,' the Colonel said, 'does Lieutenant Gruber know anything?'

'René has always been very careful not to drop anything in front of him,' Yvette said.

'I find the presence of nuns very uplifting,' the Captain piped.

'In that case,' the Colonel said, 'we must go.'

19 APRIL

Edith, apparently, has been putting herself about a bit. It can't have been with the Germans, or they would have surrendered immediately.

'I am so proud of her,' said the mother of my widow. 'They were round her like flies.'

'I expect her hat has gone off,' I said.

Beneath this jovial exterior, however, lies a very worried hero of the Resistance. I'm not frightened of the Gestapo. I'm not frightened of being shot again. But my widow scares out of me the living daylights. She is spending my money like water. And the worst thing of all is that if I want to get my restaurant back, I may even have to marry the old bat all over again.

Michelle of the Resistance provides the only spark of hope. She will return imminently to collect the two British airmen. I find I admire her and more and more, having seen her in action. I wonder if she would ever

with me. Perhaps, but probably only once.*

* *Michelle seems regularly to have followed René's lead during this period, so this reference remains confusing. It is possible that the missing section of the journal would reveal what was on his mind.*

20 APRIL

Helga tells me Herr Flick opened his raincoat to her in the Colonel's office yesterday evening to reveal something of enormity to her. An unusually large knockwurst, emblazoned with a little swastika.

In it, he explained, was the real painting of The Fallen Madonna by Van Clomp, which he wants me to hide in my kitchen. He has another containing the forgery he wishes the Colonel to send to the Fuhrer in Berlin.

The third painting he found too hot to handle, so destroyed it in a very large furnace. It seems everything is too hot to handle these days. Now that I am a single man, Yvette and Maria both

explosive, hidden in the broom cupboard.* And what's more, Hubert Gruber has presented me with a little luxury gift from Gay Paris. A charming cologne, very popular with the tank corps: lily of the valley, with a hint of diesel oil.

* *Yet again we glimpse our hero at the centre of affairs. It is extraordinary that anything so likely to blow up in his face should be hidden in the broom cupboard, but it is another sign of René's bravery. Besides, he had probably tried everywhere else.*

Maria goes weak at the knees when René shows her the whereabouts of something explosive

21 APRIL

Helga has concocted a plan of such audacity that only I can carry it out. Unknown, of course, to Herr Flick, we are going to send the Fuhrer a forged knockwurst containing no painting. The real knockwurst containing the forged painting will be stamped with a forged swastika and hung in my kitchen. The real knockwurst with the real painting stamped with the real swastika will be hidden in my cellar and sold after the war.

I have to cook the forged knockwurst, which will then be put on a train to Berlin. I am to tell my fellow heroes of the Resistance that there are valuable secret military supplies on the train and they will blow it up. If I don't, I will be shot.

Leclerc (for it is he)
delivers the knockwurst

Oh well, I suppose it will save me from having to woo Edith for a while. At least for the twenty-two-and-a-half minutes it will take to cook the knockwurst.

22 APRIL

Leclerc, the forger, arrived yesterday evening disguised as a simple village idiot. I congratulated him on his most convincing role yet.

'You will rendezvous at the cowshed of Farmer Claude at one o'clock tonight,' he said. Luckily he said it only once because manure formed a large part of his cover, and the smell was beginning to get to me.

'I won't,' I replied.

For some reason, Edith, who was eavesdropping on my briefing, jumped to the conclusion that I, who had died for France once already this year, was a coward. And a coward she could not marry.

We were there at a quarter to. The airmen were already in the shed, waiting to be milked. They were dressed as a pantomime cow. Disguised as a mushroom picker, I had to lead them and five other cows across a road heavily

Curse Repote: *Crabtree*

This curse lasted for six whacks, and dolt with all aspics of longwodge and disgeese. Successful gradiots will be folly trooned to piss as a native, moaning, noon and nit.

Disgees: God

Escape plons: God

Longwodge: Very god — farty out of fifty. His French cod not be butter.

Roodio: Spook well.

Massage from the headmooster: This gradiot pissed out with tap marks for fartitude. He is completely fat to go aboot the bosness of a French poloceman. God lick!

guarded by Germans. Edith was behind me with a gun.

It was not my lucky night. The plane arrived on time, but did not land. Instead it dropped the packages by parachute. One was an escape package for the two airmen; the other was another British idiot who speaks French like my widow cooks.

Then one of the cows dropped another two packages on my foot.

After much concentration and some help from Yvette, I learn that the new man is saying his name is Crabtree and that he is a secret intelligence officer, which is why he is disguised as a gendarme. Judging from his performance so far, he keeps his intelligence very secret indeed.

Before leading the pantomime cow back to Farmer Claude's, I outlined to Michelle my audacious plan to blow up the Berlin train. Not for the first time since she has been under my command, she asked me to listen very carefully.

'No,' she said.

Not for the first time, I got the feeling that I might have to get on the job myself.

24 APRIL

Sure enough, this very evening I found myself in the turret of Lieutenant Gruber's little tank, with the Captain at the wheel.

The plan was very simple. We were to make our way to the railway track, fire one of the Lieutenant's twenty-millimetre shells at the ammunition truck of the Berlin Express, thereby destroying both the train and the forged knockwurst, and return before the Lieutenant and the Colonel finished dinner. It was Helga's plan. I'm beginning to think there is more to her than meets the eye.

I can't claim that the mission was a complete success.

When we headed home half an hour later, we had blown up one signal box, destroyed the Colonel's car and lost the cologne and ladies' underwear from the Lieutenant's glove box. Unfortunately we left the train – and the forged knockwurst – intact.

An hour later, we had been shot at by the Resistance, foiled Michelle's plan to blow up an ammunition lorry, and watched Otto Flick blow up his own staff car.

'And worst of all,' Lieutenant Gruber wailed, 'there are nasty little dents all over my little tank and the wheels are covered in mud.'

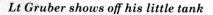

Lt Gruber shows off his little tank

This morning the Colonel and the Captain were good enough to drop in at the café on their way to Switzerland. They didn't want to wait and see how the Fuhrer was going to react to their present of an empty knockwurst.

It was going to take a special kind of courage to make that journey; dressed as Frenchmen, carrying little more than the week's payroll for the garrison and the original painting of the Fallen Madonna with the Big Boobies by Van Clomp. For a moment, I was tempted to go with them.

We were sharing a last cognac when that stupid fool Crabtree came in.

'I have good nose,' he said.

'Yes, you are very handsome,' I replied. 'Now go away.'

'The troon carrying the sausage was bummed by the RAF.'

'Bummed by the RAF?' I said.

'Bummed by the RAF?' Lieutenant Gruber asked, forgetting for a moment about his armoured car.

'I think he means bombed,' I said, wishing to let Hubert down gently.

'Yes, in a grote big poof –' Crabtree said.

'– of smoke, Hubert, of smoke,' I said.

'What a pity,' the Colonel beamed. 'I think that calls for a drink.'

My widow is continuing to dress herself up like the dinner of a dog and parade around the town square in search of suitors. It is beginning to worry me. Not half as much as it should worry them, but that is little consolation.

Yvette, on the other hand, is a lot of consolation. I took her in the back-room this afternoon

collapsible sofa.

Unfortunately, I was more exhausted than I realised by the previous night's activities so   my will   and left it to her.*

At that moment, Michelle of the Resistance and the stupid fool Crabtree climbed in through the window.

'The escape package brought by this British agent was damaged in the landing. You must help to mend it,' Michelle said.

'Mend it?' I replied. 'I don't even know what it is.'

'It is a balloon made of silk. Filled with hot air, it will lift the airmen in the basket and, with a favourable wind, take them back across the channel.'

'If you want an unfavourable wind, you could take the mother of my widow as well.' I suddenly felt much more cheerful.

'But some of the fabric is torn away and missing. We will need silk to replace it,' Michelle said.

'You must go and get your hands on girls' knockers,' Crabtree announced. For a moment, I began to think he wasn't as stupid as he looked.

---

* Another mention of the collapsible sofa. It is obviously a piece of some value, and René was making absolutely sure that his will would be followed to the letter.

My Dear Madame Edith

    Please marry me. I am a man of substance. I have my mortuary, a butcher's shop, the lease of the barbers and five thousand shares in Volkswagen. Whichever way the war goes, you will be provided for.

    Your loving undertaker with the twenty-four hour service

Alfonse.

'He means knickers,' Michelle said.

'Even better,' said I. Perhaps we could start by asking Yvette. She would probably give me one for France, or even better, a pair. I resolved to get on the job immediately.

27 APRIL

Nouvion is witnessing signs of patriotism that must do every Frenchman's heart proud. All the girls in the Resistance have sacrificed their knickers, and as far as I have been able to ascertain, with very little hesitation.

28 APRIL

Yvette, spurred on no doubt by the example of her companions, has now given up her entire supply.* It is very satisfying.

29 APRIL

Just when I thought things were finally going my way, Edith has to ruin it. I found her entertaining a suitor in the restaurant today, and he was very familiar.

'Monsieur Alfonse has come to ask for my hand in marriage,' she said.

'But what has an old undertaker got to offer?' I asked.

At this, he took out a list. 'I have, as you know, my own establishment. Since the war, business has been very brisk. I have two hearses and four horses. I have in stock twenty-six ready-made coffins. I have seventy-two metres of planed oak, stocks of elm and pine, twenty-six marble angels, twelve concrete cherubs, fifty kilos of assorted

---

* My mother is still like that. 'René,' she would say to me as I grew up, 'charity begins at home.'

handles and twenty-six litres of embalming fluid.'

'Oh René,' said Maria as she poured Monsieur Alfonse another cognac, 'how romantic!' I wondered why he had to come to my café to get pickled.

'I should mention that I also have a small hearse with a smaller horse –'

'Very handy for shopping,' I said.

'– I live in a luxury apartment above the mortuary and I aim one day to have a little crematorium of my own.'

'Well, Edith,' I said, 'at least if you get taken suddenly in the night, you won't have far to go.' What I didn't say was that if the early days of our marriage were anything to go by, it would be Monsieur Alfonse who would end up on the slab.

30 APRIL

I must admit that the undertaker has left us with plenty to ponder upon, as well as more than a faint smell of embalming fluid. I found myself thinking wistfully of Hubert's cologne. But not that wistfully.

I found myself also thinking that Edith's offer to keep me on as barman when she married Monsieur Alfonse was too much to take lying down. I went to ask Yvette for her advice.

1 MAY

The back room is covered with silk knickers. I haven't seen such a sight since the Nouvion Rangers came to the café to celebrate winning the cup in '38. I remember their Captain telling me they had never had such a good score. Yvette, Maria and Michelle of the Resistance are hard at it, sewing them all together to mend the balloon.

That old fool Leclerc, the forger, is still doing his bit. He came back this afternoon with a pair big enough to make a whole new balloon.

'This was my finest hour,' he said.

I'll admit I was surprised. It looked like at least an hour and a half.

Unfortunately one of our group must have overstepped his brief. Helga reported to the Colonel – and worse still, the Gestapo – that her own knickers had been removed in the garden, when she was not even looking. The red ones, with the little swastikas embroidered on the edge. Not that I had ever seen them.

The Colonel was despatched to the café to track down the culprit. I was trapped. There was only one way out. I did it for France.

'Colonel,' I said, 'it is very simple. We need silk, which is in very short supply, to make a wedding dress.'

'A wedding dress?' he said. 'How romantic! Who is it for?'

'For me,' I replied. 'I am to be married to Edith.'

There were a lot of tears, of course, for it was a very emotional moment. Lieutenant Gruber took it particularly hard, and so did Yvette and Maria.

I'm sad to say that Monsieur Alfonse took it hardest of all. 'Monsieur,' he said coldly, 'you have humiliated me. You have insulted me. I demand satisfaction.'

'I don't suppose you'd settle for the flying helmet and the egg-whisk, would you?' I said hopefully.

His response was to slap me with his glove and hand me his card. 'Swiftly and with style,' it proclaimed. I had a nasty feeling he was looking for business.

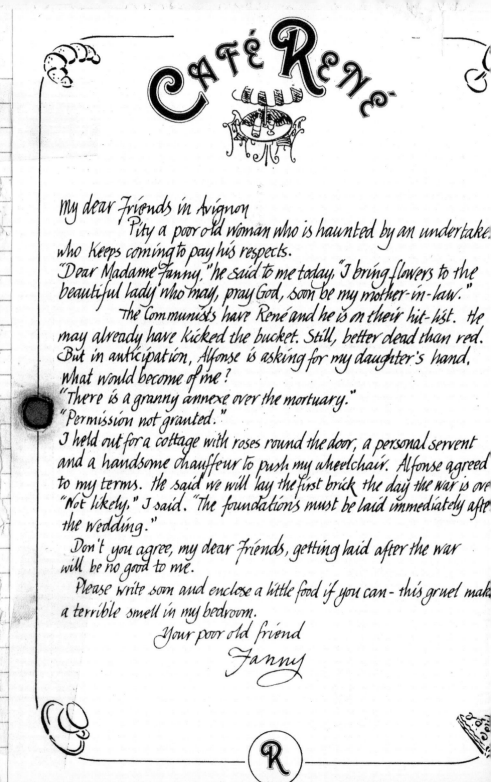

CAFÉ RENÉ

My dear Friends in Avignon

Pity a poor old woman who is haunted by an undertaker who keeps coming to pay his respects.

"Dear Madame Fanny," he said to me today, "I bring flowers to the beautiful lady who may, pray God, soon be my mother-in-law."

The Communists have René and he is on their hit-list. He may already have kicked the bucket. Still, better dead than red. But in anticipation, Alfonse is asking for my daughter's hand. What would become of me?

"There is a granny annexe over the mortuary."

"Permission not granted."

I held out for a cottage with roses round the door, a personal servent and a handsome chauffeur to push my wheelchair. Alfonse agreed to my terms. He said we will lay the first brick the day the war is over. "Not likely," I said. "The foundations must be laid immediately after the wedding."

Don't you agree, my dear friends, getting laid after the war will be no good to me.

Please write soon and enclose a little food if you can - this gruel makes a terrible smell in my bedroom.

Your poor old friend

Fanny

I have spent much of the last twenty-four hours hiding in the hen-house, and I must admit I feel like a bit of a turkey. I just can't help thinking that it would be a terrible waste if a hero of the Resistance were to have his life cut short by the bullet of an ancient undertaker. Especially since I have already been shot once this year.

I realise now that despite my more or less perpetual acts of heroism for my country, I am a man who detests violence.

The cockerel was starting to give me a very strange look when I heard someone outside.

'René, it is I, Yvette. You may reveal yourself.'

Normally I would have done. But I didn't want to give the cockerel the wrong idea.

'What is happening?' I said.

'Lieutenant Gruber has accepted Monsieur Alfonse's challenge on your behalf. He defended your reputation. They were saying you have a yellow streak.'

So would they have, I thought, if they had been sitting all night on half a dozen eggs.

I returned to the café to hear Edith addressing the Colonel, the Captain and Lieutenant Gruber. 'I am most grateful to you,' she said, 'for upholding the honour of my future husband who scarpered out of the scullery window when those men arrived.'

'I'm sure René would not run away like a coward,' Hubert said. 'There will be an explanation.'

'Of course there will,' the Colonel said.

And of course there was, though it was not one of my best. 'I was trying to catch a rabbit for your dinner, Colonel.'

'All is not lost, René,' he said reassuringly. 'Lieutenant Gruber has accepted the challenge on your behalf.'

'Lieutenant Gruber is going to fight the undertaker?' I asked.

Unfortunately not. Hubert was to be my second –

never, as he put it, too far behind me. And Edith was selling tickets for the front row and worrying about the catering.

3 MAY

Today Hubert had to present my compliments to Monsieur Alfonse, and agree with him the time and the place. I suggested South America, the Christmas after next.

Edith suggested dawn tomorrow.

Dawn tomorrow it is.

I'm glad to say that the Colonel came up with a plan immediately to improve my chances of survival. He and the Captain will take the troops out on manœuvres tomorrow morning and blow the undertaker away with a twenty-five-pound shell. I should be safe unless the Captain is pulling the trigger.

Not for the first time, I reflect that war makes for some strange bedfellows, as long as you're in the right sort of mood. As I select a sturdy coal-scuttle to use as a breastplate in case of emergency, I feel better now that the German Army is behind me. Just so long as that doesn't include Lieutenant Gruber.

Yvette tells me comfortingly that Monsieur Alfonse is a crack shot, and has put one of his balls through a playing card at twenty-five paces. I'm surprised he doesn't walk with a limp.

The only piece of good news this evening is that the balloon is nearly ready, and the British airmen will soon be leaving. They are getting on my nerves even more than usual. That stupid fool Crabtree has dressed them up as gendarmes and given them a lightning course in what he calls 'the French longwodge'. I have a terrible feeling that if Crabtree is anything to go by they'll start trying to arrest people any minute.

I had another nasty moment later on. Edith interrupted me whilst I was disciplining Maria in the cupboard under the stairs. I explained to her that I was very reluctant to tear a strip off her in front of the customers.

5 MAY

I'll be honest with you. Yesterday was not a lot of fun, even for a hero of the Resistance. Edith disturbed me very early. If you saw her at that time of the morning, I think you'd know what I mean.

'Really René,' she complained when I said I thought I might have a little lie-in. 'You'd be late for your own funeral.'

Lt Gruber does his best to make an old man happy

'Not if that undertaker of yours has anything to do with it,' I quipped bravely.

I rang Monsieur Alfonse at half-past five, just in case he was in the mood to do a deal. I wasn't sure if he was fully acquainted with my reputation for heroism. He said that he was, and that yes, he would come to a special arrangement. He would bury me at trade prices.

So there I was at seven, back to back with the undertaker, a pistol in my hand and a coal scuttle between here and eternity. As I looked around at the crowd that Edith had so thoughtfully gathered, I was impressed by how cleverly the Colonel's troops had hidden themselves. I couldn't spot a single one.

'Before I start counting, René,' Lieutenant Gruber said, 'I have to tell you that the Colonel and the Captain have been arrested by the Gestapo on suspicion of having sent the Fuhrer an empty knockwurst. Experts have apparently pieced together the wreckage of the Berlin train and found not a trace of The Fallen Madonna, or either of her boobies.'

'What about the manœuvres?' I asked, slightly apprehensively.

'They have, of course, been cancelled. But do not worry, my friend. I am right behind you.'

In that case, I thought, I had no alternative but to run. I owed it to France to live and fight another day. So that is why I am writing these pages in a haystack some distance away from yesterday morning's events. I count myself lucky that I not only wore the coal-scuttle but had you, dear Diary, in my back pocket. In spite of the fact that I was zigzagging through the woods, Monsieur Alfonse still managed to put a dent in me from seventy-five paces. Yvette's warning rang in my mind. Despite his appearance, the undertaker obviously had a lot of balls.

Michelle of the Resistance chose the same haystack for a secret meeting to decide on what course of action to take next. I suggested getting me to Switzerland.

Although I think she understood my reasoning, it is not to be. I am needed too badly at the front.

'You are a vital link in the escape route of the British airmen. Their balloon is assembled and a favourable wind is expected. We will need you to take them to the rendezvous.'

'In these clothes I am a bit conspicuous,' I said. (I am still wearing a top hat and coal-scuttle.)

'Well, take off your clothes.'

'The Resistance don't mess around, do they?' I said. 'But I'm a little old-fashioned about these things. Could we not kiss and cuddle a bit first?'

I must have embarrassed her, because she suddenly pretended she had something else in mind.

'It is so you can put on your disguise,' she said.

I will stop writing and put it on.

6 MAY

I was escorted back to the café by three girls of the Resistance. My disguise was rather daring in the cirumstances: mac, beret, wig, blouse, skirt and short socks. You will appreciate why I'll admit this only once. Monsieur Alfonse, for the time being, was not a worry. Lieutenant Gruber, however, most definitely was.

I don't know why, but he spotted me immediately. 'I'd recognise those legs anywhere, René,' he said, smiling that little smile of his. 'But do not fear. Your secret is safe with me.'

'No, you do not understand,' I said.

'Yes I do, my dear René. I had an uncle with similar leanings. Every Shrove Tuesday, he would dress up as a pancake girl.'

'I suppose you think I am a coward,' I said.

'On the contrary,' he replied. 'I think it takes great courage to come out in the open and dress that way.'

Word had reached me that Herr Flick thought I might have had something to do with the Fuhrer being cheated of the painting of The Fallen Madonna, so when two

Gestapo officers goosestepped into the restaurant I had no choice but to take up Hubert's offer of a dance.

'Keep calm, René,' he said. 'A couple of turns and then I will put you in my little tank and take you back to my place until all this dies down.' He went off to warm it up.

I retreated into the back room to adjust my skirt, to be greeted by a strangely familiar whiff of embalming fluid.

'Monsieur Alfonse,' I said jovially. 'What a pleasant surprise! I expect you are wondering why I decided not to shoot you between the eyes –'

'Nonsense, my dear Artois,' he cried. 'Michelle of the Resistance has explained everything. A bumble-bee down the trousers can unsettle even the bravest man in all France. The leader of the escape route – I had no idea! Let me kiss the hem of your dress!'

Modestly, I looked round for Michelle. She had disappeared like a phantom into the little girl's room, so reluctantly, I took the credit that was due to me.

'Just tell me what to do.' The undertaker embraced me. 'I will follow you anywhere. Vive la France!'

'Vive de Gaulle,' I said.

'Who?'

'De Gaulle. The tall one with the big hooter.'

Now he has left I have nipped down into the cellar to write a page or two. I . . .

13 MAY

Helga had burst in.

'Come,' she said. 'The Colonel and Captain are being tortured in Herr Flick's dungeon. We must help them before it is too late.'

'I cannot go like this,' I said. 'I am dressed as a girl.'

'How you relax off-duty is no concern of the German Army. You have not seen the Colonel let his hair down.'

'He hasn't got much,' I replied. 'And he's nearly always wearing a flying helmet.'

It was a short trip to the dungeons of the Gestapo HQ. Engelbert Von Smallhausen, Herr Flick's sidekick, arrested me on the way out of the café. He almost didn't let me bring my handbag.

I will try to draw a veil over the terrible week that followed. The ceiling of the dungeon descended at a signal from Herr Flick, almost crushing us. We had to watch, helpless, as he played with his organ. The Colonel and the Captain took their death pills, which failed to work. My lipstick got smudged.

In the nick of time we were liberated by the very man who had ordered my previous execution. General Von Klinkerhoffen, whose opinion of the Gestapo clearly matches my own, shot the lock off the dungeon door in a fit of rage.

'You cannot do this,' Flick shouted. 'My godfather is Heinrich Himmler.'

Klinkerhoffen was unimpressed. 'My wife's sister is the mistress of Hermann Goering,' he replied. 'The one who wears chamois leather underclothes.'

Fascinated as I was by this exchange, I felt it was time to leave.

'Ladies first,' I said.

War makes for some strange bedfellows

General Von Klinkerhoffen has ordered that the Colonel's manœuvres be resumed.

'The town is ringed with German soldiers. We are under curfew,' Yvette told me breathlessly. I suggested a quiet night in.

Michelle had other ideas. She is always coming to the café with some excuse or other. I have had a terrible feeling since the episode in the haystack that her feelings for me are not simply those of an innocent young girl towards a hero of the Resistance.

This very same afternoon I found myself disguised as an undertaker, smuggling the two British airmen in one of Monsieur Alfonse's hearses. The wind was in the right direction, finally, for England.

The undertaker spoke the words a grateful nation knew would embarrass me: 'I cannot say what an honour it is for me to assist you, Monsieur René – the bravest man in France, who has just escaped death by Gestapo torture and without thought of his personal danger, is even now helping the British airmen to escape.'

'Can I have that in writing?' I asked.

'Only if you write it,' said Edith, inexplicably. 'It is not your plan, it is the plan of Michelle. If you had your way, you would be in bed.'

'Of course,' Monsieur Alfonse said. 'As a lover he is also a legend.'

'You are too kind,' I said.

'Yes he is,' echoed Edith.

General Von Klinkerhoffen himself cut her short by halting the cortège and opening one of the three coffins to check if we were on our way to a real funeral. Fortunately he chose the casket occupied by my widow's mother. One look was enough. White-faced and shaking, he waved us on.

The airmen filled the balloon and floated into the gathering dusk. 'Thanks awfully for having us,' they said, whatever that means. I was almost sad to see them go.

15 MAY

No I wasn't. They're back.

The wind changed direction, and one shot from Von Klinkerhoffen's pistol convinced the idiots to turn off the burner, so they wouldn't be seen in the dark. They crashed through the ceiling of the bedroom of my widow's mother early this morning, just as we were getting her back out of her coffin.

It is now even more draughty in there than usual.

16 MAY

General Von Klinkerhoffen has taken personal command of all troops in the Nouvion district. My heroic Resistance activities have apparently delayed the Fuhrer's victory for many months, and the High Command is worried.

The Colonel isn't too happy either. He has been told by the General that he is short of intelligence, and what's worse, has been ordered to have an affair with Edith to try and improve the situation.

I have to say I didn't immediately see the connection, but Captain Geering tells me that Von Klinkerhoffen believes that amorous liaisons with local girls pay good dividends.

'We have tried this,' the Colonel told him.

'Lots of times,' piped the Captain.

'Did you learn anything new?' asked the General.

'One or two things,' they admitted, but it wasn't enough to get them off the hook.

18 MAY

Hans looked rather glum when he came in for his usual.

'A hard day at the office, Captain?' I asked as I placed a carafe of fine house wine at his disposal.

'I should coco. We have a new intake of privates at the barracks. They are very badly trained. When they are given the order to stand to attention, they stand at ease. When they are told to stand at ease, they fall out. It is a shambles.'

'Trouble?' asked Lieutenant Gruber, pulling up a chair.

'It is the Colonel,' I said. 'He is having a bit of trouble with his privates.'

'Oh?'

'Yes, they keep falling out.'

'Has he tried a change of clothing?'

'Yes,' said Hans, 'but that did no good. Now General Von Klinkerhoffen has told him to clap them in irons. The Colonel is very worried.'

'I imagine he would be. I have a designer friend in Berlin from my window-dressing days I could refer him to . . .'

23 MAY

It's been a quiet week for business, so I decided this morning to put in a bit of time on the billiard table with Yvette. When I arrived in the games room I was slightly surprised to discover that she had already started.

'I was just practising, René,' she said. 'Look at this position. I am right up against the cushion and have no alternative but to screw the length of the table.'

Not for the first time I realised there was very little I could teach Yvette.

We had hardly started the session when Edith and Michelle arrived. My fellow heroes of the Resistance had decided that they could not operate under the cruel tyranny of General Von Klinkerhoffen. He had to be killed.

Edith had a plan. 'René, you could deliver him some food and round your waist you could strap dynamite, and when you got near him you could light the fuse and – whoof – he would be gone and you would be buried as a great hero of the Resistance.'

I had a plan too. It involved checking the effectiveness of the escape route to Switzerland.

24 MAY

Herr Flick and Helga also have a plan. I had my ear to the keyhole of the back room whilst they were entertaining each other last night. I often do this. It is my way of monitoring the enjoyment of my customers without imposing myself upon them.

On this occasion, however, they were not complimenting the cuisine. They were organising the assassination of Von Klinkerhoffen with a poisoned dart shot from a blow-pipe.

'He's about to be rubbed out,' I told Maria. 'Poof! With a cigarette holder.'

She glanced across at Lieutenant Gruber, who was tickling the ivories in the corner of the restaurant. 'And he plays the piano so beautifully,' she said sadly.

I was about to put her right when the Colonel came in. He has not been to the café since Von Klinkerhoffen ordered him to have an affair with my wife. He has finally found a solution to the problem. Or rather, two solutions.

The first was for the Captain to have the affair.

'There is not another singer like you in the whole world,' he piped when Edith had finished a number. She rewarded his gallantry with a kiss that steamed up his glasses. 'Oh Captain,' she breathed when he removed them for wiping, 'without glasses you are even more attractive.'

'So are you!' he said.

The second was to kill the General, who was clearly less popular than I had assumed. The Captain would poison him with a drug in a jug of wine at the forthcoming party at the château to celebrate the Kaiser's birthday.

25 MAY

Life is getting complicated again.

The two British airmen have found a way of phoning Wimbledon on the radio transmitter, and I'm very worried about the bill. And Edith is to bake a gâteau for the château which is to be filled with dynamite. The fuse will be a candle with a handle. I would have thought the cake alone should do the trick.

This party is going to make the burning of the Reichstag look like an evening with my wife's mother. I have a terrible feeling it is not going to be good for business.

Carstairs and Fairfax trying to remember the number of the Wimbledon exchange

26 MAY

Now I know it is not going to be good for business. Herr Flick of the Gestapo has given instructions for the party to be held at the café instead. And everybody is invited for tomorrow night.

A Song for the Boys in the Tank Corps
(Especially "B" Troop)

If you ever get across the sea to England,
Then maybe at the closing of the day,
The bars will all be serving German lager,
Which means we've won the war
"Hip hip hooray"...

27 MAY

I could not live with the possibility that innocent heroes of
the Resistance might be killed, and in my restaurant. I
had to take action.

Von Klinkerhoffen borrowed Helga's cigarette holder
before she could use it on him, so Herr Flick took the dart
on the nose instead. But then I had to deal with the drug
in the jug and the candle with the handle on the gâteau
for the château.

After swopping the Captain's poison pill with an
aspirin, things were still desperate. The General lit the
candle with the handle and the fire bucket was the only
answer.

I'm not sure he was overjoyed when I covered the
gateau with a pile of sand. 'You fool,' he screamed. 'We
were celebrating the moment of the Kaiser's birth!'

'I meant no disrespect, General,' I said cleverly. 'I am
celebrating the moment of his heroic burial.'

31 MAY

This war is starting to take its toll. It is three days since
Le Café René narrowly avoided becoming a five-star hole
in the ground, and my nerves still need considerable
soothing. I was luxuriating in a warm bath this morning
and Yvette, ever solicitous, asked if I was ready for two big
jugs. I was.

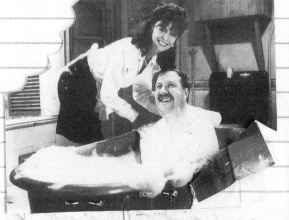

Yvette lets René
have it with both jugs

'Sorry it took so long, René,' she said. 'The old boiler is in a terrible state.'

'I don't know why I married her in the first place,' I replied.

I had scarcely begun to enjoy the second jug when there was a knock on the window. It was Michelle.

'I shall say this only once,' she said, 'because I am clinging to a rusty drainpipe. I have a plan to get rid of the British airmen –'

Unluckily for her the drainpipe gave way before she could go any further.

Later on I found myself telling Lieutenant Gruber about the difficulties of finding sufficient privacy to attend to one's toilet. He was very understanding.

'I have a very large bath at the château if you ever want to indulge yourslf, René.'

I suddenly decided to change the subject. 'Excuse me, Lieutenant,' I said. 'I can't help noticing that my wife has just finished one of her songs. Some of my other customers may need help.'

'She has an unusual voice,' he said, unwilling to lose me. 'Was it trained?'

'It was,' I replied. 'But it escaped and returned to the wild.'

1 JUNE

Michelle of the Resistance did not have a happy landing
yesterday. She appeared last night with her leg in plaster,
supported by that fool Crabtree who thinks he can speak
our language. Her plan is to steal a plane with no engine
from the Nouvion Transport Museum, fix it up with the
engine from General Von Klinkerhoffen's motor mower,
and bingo, no airmen.

I wondered whether she had taken a sharp blow to the
head as well. 'Who will steal this plane?' I asked, knowing
that she would find it hard to entrust a task like this to
anyone else.

I was right.

'You will,' she whispered only once.

2 JUNE

I had my ear to the keyhole of the back room at lunchtime,
anxious to know Herr Flick's opinion of the *Culotte de
Bœuf René aux Flageolets* when I overheard a conversation
of a rather different kind.

'I have bad news,' Von Smallhausen reported. 'The
Resistance have kidnapped your knockwurst and are
demanding a ransom for its return. I received this
information at ten o'clock this morning.'

'That was four hours ago,' Flick said coldly. 'Why did
you take so long to inform me?'

'This message was wrapped round a brick and thrown
at my head. I have only just regained consciousness.'

'It is very serious. Helga, your Colonel is in charge of
security. Tell him that if the knockwurst is not recovered
he is to burn down Nouvion – except for this building.'

I had a sudden image of *Le Café René* standing in the
midst of the ashes, the only café for miles around. It was
dreadful news, but I resolved to make the best of it.

3 JUNE

It is the Communist Resistance causing all the trouble, as usual. They want eight thousand francs before they return what Herr Flick thinks is the real painting of The Fallen Madonna with the Big Boobies by Van Clomp. If the money is not found, the sausage will be sliced. If the sausage is sliced, the town will burn.

Edith tells me that Monsieur Alfonse has eight thousand francs hidden in his mattress. How she found this out, I can only guess.

She is at this very moment attempting to persuade the old man to lend it to us so that we can give it to the Communists in return for the painting and then ambush them and get it back.

I'd rather not speculate on how she intends to do it, but I know that for some reason my wife makes him feel like a man twenty years younger. I should think he does the same for her.

4 JUNE

Things didn't quite go according to plan.

Edith got the money from Monsieur Alfonse. The Communist Resistance got the money from us. Unfortunately one of Lieutenant Gruber's very large dogs got the knockwurst, and because the ambush was a complete failure we will never see the eight thousand francs again either.

In future I must take responsibility for everything myself. I should know by now that whilst it is all very well having people under me, I should never let them take the lead.

5 JUNE

How do you tell an old undertaker with a weak heart that his entire life savings have gone? By phone, I suppose.

I'm not a man to delay things, but I might leave it until next week.

12 JUNE

It has not been an easy week for Lieutenant Gruber either. As he was taking his little tank out for a spin this afternoon he dropped by the café to tell me about it.

'Herr Flick is not pleased that my dog, Eric, stole his sausage. "Gruber," he said, "have you been mincing?"'

'Well, had you?'

'Of course. Eric only likes his knockwurst chopped up very finely.'

'What about the painting?'

'He wasn't too happy about that either, until I told him that actually it was a forgery.'

Somehow I don't think we've heard the last of The Fallen Madonna with the Big Boobies.

13 JUNE

I was right.

Herr Flick is under the impression that there is a certain hero of the Resistance not a million miles away from here who had something to do with his Van Clomp being switched with a forgery. He has ordered Lieutenant Gruber to drive his little tank from where it is parked outside the front of the café into the garden at the back. In a straight line.

I had to think fast. I realised that I would have to tell Hubert the truth about the paintings.

'How would it be if we substituted another forgery in another sausage?' he suggested. 'I think I could provide a copy if I could see the original.'

'I didn't know you were an artist,' I said.

'I have leanings, you know,' he replied, 'and not a little talent. Before I was a window dresser I was employed in an art gallery. Occasionally I was allowed to touch up old masters.'

With that, he asked if we could go down to the cellar to look at my masterpiece. I can see this is going to be very complicated.

23 JUNE

I haven't had time for writing much recently. The mid-year accounts have been occupying most of my waking thoughts.

Yvette's and Maria's figures have been holding up well, and in some areas have even shown signs of improvement. Losses in other parts of the business, however, have been appalling. This has partly to do with the fact that Edith has been spending most of the bar takings on hats. The rest I blame on Monsieur Alfonse. I paid him back eight thousand francs forged by the idiot Leclerc, and he promptly went and spent them in the café as a tribute to my heroism.

24 JUNE

Lieutenant Gruber was very anxious that I bring the real painting of The Fallen Madonna to his room in the château so he could start on the copy. I had a shrewd suspicion I might get invited to stay on and see his etchings.

Unfortunately I was far too busy today to go myself, and sent Maria instead, with the canvas concealed about her bosom. She has been captured by General Von Klinkerhoffen, who did not believe that she had an appointment with Lieutenant Gruber even when she showed him the knockwurst.

So now both Maria and the knockwurst, which is a whopper, are imprisoned in the General's wardrobe, and he is demanding the return of the engine of his motor mower in return for their freedom. And without the engine we won't be able to rid ourselves of the two British airmen.

It will take a genius to get them out.

25 JUNE

I spent a lot of last night hiding under General Von Klinkerhoffen's bed with Yvette. It was touch and go, I must say, and at one stage, as I explained to Edith when she found us there, I had to revive the young girl with the heat of my body. She had fainted with excitement.

Suffice it to say that my daring undercover work paid off, and both Maria and the knockwurst are now safely back in the cellar of the café. I must go down and see if she is any the worse for her ordeal.

26 JUNE

Michelle of the Resistance is still wedded to this hare-brained scheme to steal the aeroplane without the engine. There is one big problem, however: it is at the very back of the Transport Museum, with many antique vehicles in the way. She has spent most of the time since her accident trying to think of a way round.

I told her that I'd be prepared to forget the whole thing. I'm pretty sure that General de Gaulle, the one with the big hooter, will be calling on the transmitter any minute to award me a whole string of medals – so what's one more?

*Yvette dusts up her technique
in the General's bedroom*

27 JUNE

She has found a way. The Germans have given permission
for us to hold an Antique Vehicle Rally tomorrow. The
plan is to move everything out of the way of the plane,
insert the engine from the mower, then attach it to a car
with a very long piece of elastic. The car will be driven
from the museum at great speed by a hero of the
Resistance, thereby catapulting the two British airmen
back across the Channel.

There was a call from London this morning. I thought
it was de Gaulle, but he is obviously still busy thinking
about my medals. In fact it was the C.O. of the two airmen,
Wing Commander Randy Hargreaves. He is desperate for
them to return immediately. The war must be going very
badly for them.

A message also arrived from Lieutenant Gruber. He
wanted to get his hands on The Fallen Madonna. This was

a bit of a turn up.

I invited him into the back room. 'A rare honour, René,' he beamed as he came in. 'It is the first time I have seen your rear quarters. This is very cosy.'

Before he got any cosier, I suggested we go upstairs and find the knockwurst containing the painting, which I had hidden in my bed. This seemed very popular with the Lieutenant.

I was horrified to see that Edith had got there first. Even worse, she was in the process of giving the knockwurst a little nibble.*

'What are you doing with that sausage?' I cried.

'I prayed to God and he left it under my bed.'

'You prayed to God for a sausage?' This was a new one on me.

'No,' she replied, 'but this was obviously as near as He could get.'

'Rationing,' I said to Lieutenant Gruber on the way down, 'can be very frustrating.'

30 JUNE

It is not usual for a hero of the Resistance to complain, but my body has taken a lot of punishment in the last few days. In fact I am being tended to by Yvette as I write, so forgive me if my hand starts to wander.

We collected enough braces from the patriots of Nouvion to make the catapult for the plane. They had been dropping them in the bar for the last twenty-four hours, and Lieutenant Gruber couldn't believe his luck.

I bared my torso for France on the afternoon of the Antique Vehicle Rally, disguised as a road mender. There

* I know how easy this can be.

was only one nasty moment when the Lieutenant appeared in his little tank and pointed his big gun at me.

Soon Michelle signalled that all the obstacles had been cleared and the plane was ready for take-off. I got into the car and moved it skilfully through the gears. I was soon travelling at an incredible speed, with the elastic stretching out behind me. As I turned to wave at Yvette and Maria, the earth moved.

I thought at first that Edith, who was in the passenger seat, had given me a sharp blow to the head. In fact the chocks had jammed in front of the aircraft's wheels and a very unhappy hero of the Resistance was catapulted back into the Transport Museum.

I don't know where my wife landed, but there was some suggestion afterwards that she be placed on permanent display as an intercontinental ballistic missile.

30 JULY

There cannot be many French café-owners languishing in a prisoner-of-war camp in the borrowed uniform of a British Flight Lieutenant, and it is a little unusual even for a hero of the Resistance.

How did I get here? It's a long story, but since paper is so scarce in this place I will cut it very short. I'll only go back about seventy years or so to when my wife's mother was having it off in Avignon with a weirdo from Holland she called Bobby. Bobby was a painter, but a very unsuccessful one. The story goes that the poor fellow was so hungry he once even ate one of his own ears. My own theory is that it was a last-ditch attempt to escape the nagging of my wife's mother. Anyway his paintings were awful. Not very lifelike at all. He seemed to specialise in close-ups of sunflowers and wobbly old chairs. That's the impression I get, anyway.

Now, one of his terrible efforts was called the Cracked Vase with the Big Daisies. He gave it to my wife's mother as a memento one day just before he went out into the sunflower field and blew his head off. Looking at early pictures of my wife's mother, I can understand his desperation.

Anyway, this is the painting which hangs in the café, and behind which yesterday I hid the painting of The Fallen Madonna with the Big Boobies by Van Clomp when all the world and his wife seemed to be hunting for it. General Von Klinkerhoffen, too, was on the hunt – for the two British airmen. But he didn't find them. They were hiding in the café, disguised as French tarts. They melted easily into the crowd.

The General did spot, however, the painting of the Cracked Vase with the Big Daisies, and he requisitioned it. He thinks it was done by someone called Vincent Van Gogh and has commmissioned Lieutenant Gruber to make a copy of it. Good luck to him, I say. There's no acounting for taste.

Meanwhile, Monsieur Alfonse was busy tunnelling from his mortuary towards the prisoner-of-war camp so that the two airmen could be smuggled into it for safe keeping. The tunnelling was not progressing fast enough for my liking, however. I got my tool out and asked Yvette what she thought of it. She seemed impressed, and asked me if she could have a go with it. I always knew that little pick would come in handy one day.

Unfortunately, the Colonel and the Captain discovered the tunnel while Edith, Yvette, Maria and I were all down it. The tunnel collapsed behind them, and we had no alternative but to surface in the camp.

Now how can I get out of here? Your guess is as good as mine. In my experience British Flight Lieutenants don't have a very good record for getting out of anywhere.

31 JULY

I spent most of today holding my trousers open at the top while Yvette and Edith filled them up with soil.

You will find this hard to believe, but the German guards (or 'goons' as we British Flight Lieutenants prefer to call them) then found nothing suspicious about the hang of my trousers as I waddled out of the hut nearly a hundred times like the Michelin man with haemorrhoids, undid my cycle clips, and then walked all around the vegetable patch while shaking my legs vigorously. If they don't find that sort of behaviour just a little bit worth looking into then I reckon they deserve to lose the war. Or maybe it's just that they understand the ways of the British better than I.

Ah me, will there ever be an end to the madness of war, I ask myself? Will there ever be an end to the unrelenting hardship and danger of digging this tunnel? And more to the point, will there ever be an end to the merciless chafing of my soiled underwear?

Whatever happens, I must get out of here soon. The café opens at six o'clock and I have a business to run. And *merde!* I am now down to writing on toilet paper.

1 AUGUST

Another day, another hundred trouser-loads of earth.

Edith was beginning to get decidedly edgy. 'I hope I am not expected to sleep in this hut with forty desperate men,' she said.

'They are only desperate to get out, Edith,' I muttered.

But there was no need for her to get her hideous French knickers in a twist. While shaking out his trousers in the vegetable patch a humble Normandy café-owner had had a blinding flash, and even as his wife spoke he was sketching it out in his diary for the British escape committee.

2 AUGUST

Tonight I am to be a Bluebell Girl in the Camp Concert – and with a title like that to the show, I can't help feeling how lucky it is that Lieutenant Gruber is otherwise engaged.

It has been quite a busy day, rehearsing my high kick routine and timing my splits to perfection. Luckily carrying around all that earth from the tunnel has done marvellous things for my legs. I will certainly be able to be much more energetic next time Yvette needs my help in the cellar.

The Colonel and the Captain took to the cricket field

this afternoon, but by all accounts the cricket field did not take to them. The game ended when the Commandant's window got broken, and the Commandant got very cross. Shortly afterwards, Captain Hans went for the big one over square leg with the help of the plank across the barrel and yours truly off the hut roof with half a ton of soil in his trousers. He should be on his way now to fetch Lieutenant Gruber's little tank so that he can smash down the wire and rescue us.

Oh, what a lovely war!

3 AUGUST

Well that's show business for you. One moment you are a star and the next you are on the rubbish heap. Lieutenant Gruber has rescued us by disguising himself as a dustcart driver and taking us away amongst the tea-leaves and old

fish-heads. Heaven only knows what Fate holds in store for us now. I suppose I could always read the tea-leaves to find out.

It appears that the brilliant rescue plan was both his and Helga's. They took the view that we are in this together: we all share an interest, after all, in certain paintings which we will sell after the war. Besides, Gruber felt the café was just not the same without me.

To get the message to us about their plan, one of them had appeared at the camp gate dressed like Marlene Dietrich, in a brimmed hat and raincoat which opened to reveal lascivious underwear and a lot of leg. Much to my surprise, it was not Gruber. *He* was dressed as a nun.

Well, everything went according to plan – except for one little thing. The two British airmen who were supposed to stay behind in the camp followed us into the dustcart and have escaped as well. So now we're right back to square one. What's more, the Colonel is now sitting in my cellar, dressed as a girl from the Folies Bergères.

He cannot leave, even in borrowed clothes, because of the curfew. And we've also heard that the Captain has been taken away by the Communist Resistance. Michelle thought they were on strike, but apparently they've settled for higher ransoms.

Maria did not escape with us. Michelle has just brought news of her. She broke into the postal room of the prisoner-of-war camp and disguised herself as a Red Cross parcel. Unfortunately she did not put on enough stamps so she has been sent back to Switzerland. So now we must advertise for a new girl. Is there no end to it?

4 AUGUST

No, there isn't. We also nearly got nicked last night by Herr Flick. He, along with that overgrown fruit-bat, Von Smallhausen, had climbed onto the roof of Gestapo headquarters and jammed the broadcast from London, substituting a message of their own.

Of course, we weren't to know that. ''Allo Nighthawk, we wish to send medals to the members of the Resistance,' came the totally innocent request. 'Please give me their names and addresses.'

I had to give the honest answer. 'We do not know their names and addresses, but send me the medals and I will pass them on.'

It was then that they made the sort of mistake that a highly alert Resistance brain was able to detect at once. In the backgound I heard a strange sliding noise and Von Smallhausen's suddenly receding voice. 'Herr Flick,' he observed as he plummeted into space, 'I am falling off the roof . . .'

In the heat of the moment and for the good of France, I threw the radio out of the window. It is my wife that we must then thank for coming up with idea of using the radio in Lieutenant Gruber's little tank to continue our conversation with London. To create a diversion, I got the

Lieutenant to sing me a song at the piano. His choice was
Mad About The Boy. Well it would be, wouldn't it? He fixed
his eyes on me as he sang. It wasn't going to be easy to
get away.

  'Lieutenant Gruber, your singing is so beautiful I will
have to go outside. I do not like crying in front of men.'

  'I understand,' he said. 'I feel quite emotional myself.'

  On that note, I went to join the others in Lieutenant
Gruber's little tank. Unfortunately, the idiot policeman
who thinks he can speak our language overheard the noise
of the radio and reported us to the Colonel. He caught us
red-handed.

DESIRABLE OPENINGS IN SERVICE INDUSTRY

Busy Nouvion Café Seeks Versatile Girls with Friendly Personalities

Owing to a massive upswing in trade since June 1940, the very
popular Café René is now looking for more girls with an open
approach to their work.

Whether serving in the Café, meeting customers' demands upstairs,
or helping down below with the *patron*'s other requirements, you
will be a vital member of a close-knit team.

Aged between 16 and 25, you must be physically fit and able to
wear the attractive uniform to full advantage.

Working hours flexible. Celery to be negotiated.

Applicants should be available for personal interview at any time.

  'René,' he said rather crossly, 'what are you doing in
Gruber's little tank?'

  'Well, Colonel, we heard the telephone ringing so we
just popped in to answer it. Just in case it was anyone
important for you – you know, like Hitler.'

That was definitely enough quick thinking for one humble café-owner for one day. I was ready for a bit of a lie-down. I was just looking around for Yvette when Gruber's receiver crackled and London came through again.* Who of all people should be on the other end but Captain Geering? He was in an office overlooking Piccadilly Circus. He sounded surprisingly happy. He said he wasn't coming back.

'What am I going to tell the General?' the Colonel asked.

'Tell him the food is very good and the British think they are going to win. Over and out.'

20 AUGUST

If you could see me now, dear Diary, you would be asking yourself why it is that I am wearing a clean new apron today, and why it is that I have trimmed my moustache and manicured my nails. If you were standing next to me you would know that I am also wearing a very powerful after-shave lotion. My wife finds it irresistible so I seldom wear it, but this is a special occasion. I have advertised for a girl to work under me in the bar and there have been many applicants. Today is interview day. Unfortunately, rather too many interested parties for my liking have opted themselves onto the selection committee ...

---

* *How typical of the altruism of René Artois that he should worry about the whereabouts of his staff in a moment of crisis. It is only to be hoped that he managed to find my mother and so relieve his tension.*

APPLICANT: Madame Sablon
SPECIAL ABILITIES: Elderly. Walks with a stick.
EDITH'S COMMENTS: Very suitable.
MY COMMENTS: Rejected
solely on the grounds that she
wouldn't be able to get on her
knees to scrub the floor, or
climb the stairs to entertain
the Germans.

APPLICANT: Mademoiselle Angelique Vitesse
SPECIAL ABILITIES: 38–28–38
EDITH'S COMMENTS: Next please.
MY COMMENTS: Youthful and
enthusiastic. Would have
worked well under me.

APPLICANT: Mademoiselle Valérie Vendôme
SPECIAL ABILITIES: Until recently worked in a circus.
Can ride one-wheel bicycle and perform cartwheels crabs
and other acrobatics. Also sings
beautifully and does cabaret.
EDITH'S COMMENTS: So do I.
Next please.
MY COMMENTS: Her skills
might have come in handy for
errands and dusting under the beds.

APPLICANT: Mimi Labonq
SPECIAL ABILITIES: Resistance gang leader in Paris.
Martial arts expert. Can knock café-owners to the floor
with one blow.
EDITH'S COMMENTS: Good
– she is hired.
MY COMMENTS: Michelle of
the Resistance is pointing
a gun at me.

A day of shocks, starting when Herr Flick of the Gestapo arrived with Helga in his staff car. Helga was driving.

'You drive well,' I overheard him say to her as I collected cups from the tables outside my humble café.

'Thank you, Herr Flick,' Helga replied. 'I am, however, not good at reversing.'

'You managed very well last night.'

I only just recovered in time to greet them at the door.

'Welcome to my humble café, Herr Flick,' I said. 'Let me take from you your sinister leather coat.' I led them to their usual table in the back room – only to find Crabtree behind the curtains.

'Good evening, officer,' I said. 'How comforting to know that you are doing your duty.'

'It is a dick night. I thought I saw two men leaking by your dustbins.'

'Well,' I said, 'that's France for you.'

More shocks were to follow. With my ear to the keyhole of the private dining room, I overheard the following conversation:

'Herr Flick, when you behave in such a dominating fashion I go weak at the knees.'

'Only the knees?'

'I am blushing.'

'This is normal. Helga, I wish you to know that this is a very special occasion. I have decided to marry you.'

'Herr Flick, I thought we were going to wait until after the war?'

'These are dangerous times, Helga. We must grab every moment of happiness while we can.'

'But Herr Flick, you have managed to grab it so far without getting married.'

Herr Flick drives Helga to the country . . .

. . . and shows her his knob

24 AUGUST

I met the Colonel's new assistant tonight – Captain Alberto Bertorelli. He is an Itie. An Italian unit will be going with the Germans when they invade England. Well, I suppose somebody has to take over the ice-cream business.

Bertorelli wears a lot of medals. Some for service in Abyssinia. Some for service in North Africa. Some, I suspect, simply for servicing Fiats.

When he entered the café he kissed me.

'I am just a humble peasant you understand,' I told him. 'Trying to scratch a living with my wife's mother and my wife.'

'I embrace your wife,' he said, embracing Yvette.

'I embrace your mother-in-law,' he said, embracing Edith.

Close to tears, Edith stormed from the room. I might give Bertorelli a medal of my own.

I put my ear to the keyhole tonight as Herr Flick and Helga were finishing their meal. I always like to check how my diners are getting on with each other – whether it's another bottle of champagne they'll be needing, or just two coffees.

'I have been giving much thought to the arrangements for our wedding,' I overheard Herr Flick say.

'Herr Flick,' said Helga's gentle Aryan voice, 'are you sure that deep in your heart, wherever it is, you are ready for marriage?'

'What are you saying?'

'Well, you are so young, so attractive – women are always throwing themselves at you.'

'This is true.'

'I will be consumed with jealousy. I will be breaking plates when I do the washing-up.'

'If you do that you will be punished. We will be married in a high security Gestapo chapel. As we leave the ceremony we will walk through an arch of rubber truncheons held by my Gestapo colleagues in jackboots. We will drive away in a black Gestapo limousine showered with propaganda pamphlets. We will honeymoon in a Bavarian forest. Every morning we will leave our camouflaged tent, strip naked and dive into the icy waters of a limpid dark lake.'

'Could I have time to think about it?'

Ah, just the two coffees, then.

1 SEPTEMBER

Things are looking up. A slip of the tongue by the Colonel has revealed to me that the Germans are soon to invade England. Churchill will, of course, throw in the sponge. The war will be over in a few weeks and life will return to normal at *Le Café René*.

Things are looking down.

Michelle of the Resistance came round to tell me that I need more length. The Gestapo are jamming our broadcasts to London, and to give us a stronger signal she has arranged for a kite to be constructed which will take my aerial to the required height. Mimi is in charge of collecting

Michelle tells René he needs more length

this kite from the convent. To avoid suspicion she is to be disguised as a small nun. Well, she could hardly be disguised as a big one, could she?

'Cannot you do some of this?' I asked. Little did I know that things have obviously been getting on top of her.

'Why is it that you always question my decisions?' she snapped. 'Do you think you could do my job better? Do you think you could run the Resistance keeping everyone happy? Deciding who to shoot, what to blow up, making threatening calls? Do you know what my telephone bill is every month? Why do you not go and work for the Communist Resistance and get up their noses?'

Some people find it hard to take a subordinate role.

'Now look what you have done,' said Edith. 'You have

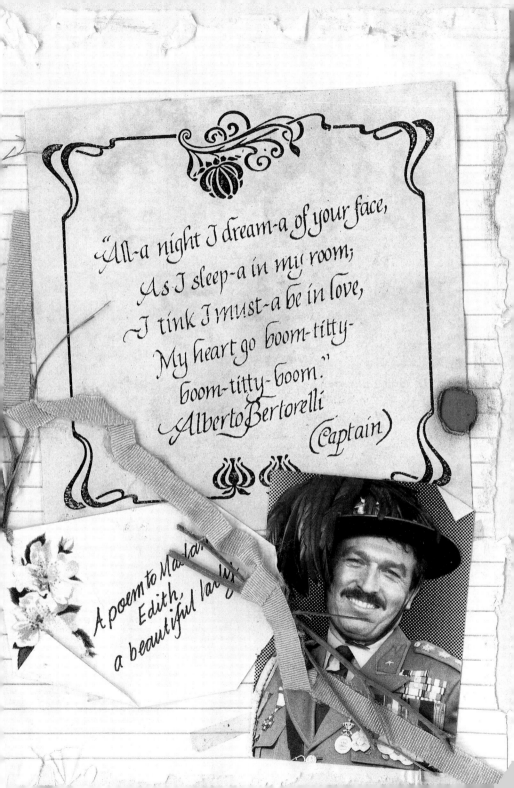

"All-a night I dream-a of your face,
As I sleep-a in my room;
I tink I must-a be in love,
My heart go boom-titty-
boom-titty-boom."
Alberto Bertorelli
(Captain)

A poem to Madam Edith, a beautiful lady

upset the Resistance.'

Luckily there was a knock at the window at that moment and Crabtree the gendarme appeared.

'Good moaning. Outside your coffee was this bunch of diffadoles and doses. Pinned to them is a nit.'

The nit was from the Italian Captain. It was a terrible poem for Edith.

'He's not the first Itie to have the hots for me,' she said glowingly.

Hah! Just because ten years ago an ice-cream man gave her a free cornet.

4 SEPTEMBER

I led Edith, Mimi and Yvette at lunchtime on an expedition to launch the kite. Edith was carrying a fully loaded picnic basket. Yvette was carrying another picnic basket containing thirty kilograms of batteries. Mimi was bent under the weight of the cripplingly heavy radio pack. I would gladly have helped them but as I explained, I have a lot of trouble with my back.

'Also you have a lot of trouble with your front,' said Edith, rather unnecessarily.

We did not know it at the time, but, as Lieutenant Gruber told me later, General Von Klinkerhoffen and the other German officers were also nearby, inspecting the area where the invasion troops would be assembling.

'That area will be occupied by one regiment of artillery,' said the General. 'In a few months' time there will be two thousand men camping there.'

'Make a note of that, Lieutenant,' said the Colonel.

'I already have,' said Gruber.

Yvette connected the wire to the kite and Edith and Mimi concealed themselves in the bushes with the radio. The moment had at last arrived for me to expose my

NIDENTIFIED FLYING NUN SIGHTED OVER NOUVION

'Baroness Von Trapp not ruled out as suspect' say Germans

leadership qualities to the full, to show these girls how willing I was to get it up for France.

Mimi handed me the large coil of wire that had been hanging on the backpack. The other end was attached to the radio. Yvette launched the kite and I ran into the wind as fast as I could. Everything went well until the kite suddenly got caught in a strong gust. The wire began to slip through my hands. It was burning my fingers. Suddenly I could hold it no longer. The rest of the coil started to unwind. When it reached the end Mimi was yanked up out of the bushes and into the sky.

'My God!' Edith screamed. 'We have lost our new waitress.'

'And good staff are so difficult to find,' I said.

14 SEPTEMBER

Michelle of the Resistance has very kindly brought round
a tandem to help me generate more volts. It will go in the
bedroom of my wife's mother, because we lost the batteries
for the radio crossing the river while rescuing Mimi the
flying nun. The dynamo will provide a temporary source
of power.

'Will not the Germans be suspicious if they search and
find a bicycle in the bedroom of my wife's mother?' I asked.

'You could say that it is a keep-fit machine.'

'Is it not a bit late? She is eighty-six.'

But it will not be for long. Already the Resistance have
stolen more batteries from a German midget submarine,
it seems. They will be delivered to me by one of her agents.

'Disguised as a torpedo I suppose?' I said.

But the good news does not stop there. More explosives
have arrived from London to be used to blow up the safe
in the château which contains the plans for the invasion.
I will have the honour of storing them in my cellar.

Really, I told her, I appreciate the fact that I am waging
a one-man war, but is it too much to ask that she lift just
a few of the more minor responsibilities from my shoulders
occasionally?

Michelle offered to have the explosives delivered
C.O.D. to save me queueing up at the post office. Another
of her agents will bring them to me concealed in a secret
pouch in his trousers.

'How will I know this man?' I enquired.

'He will be walking very gingerly,' she said.

Lieutenant Gruber came into the café this afternoon looking as if he'd just had a bit of a rough ride in his little tank.

'You may notice that I am walking very gingerly,' he said.

'Do not tell me that you have dynamite in your trousers?' I asked.

'René!' he admonished, 'do not listen to gossip!'

Herr Flick of the Gestapo also came in. At least I thought it was Herr Flick, but it turned out to be Helga, wearing his sinister leather coat and limping. She was wearing Herr Flick's clothes because he has taken hers. She brought serious news which could affect each one of us.

'Herr Flick has disguised himself as a temporary lady stenographer of the female sex. He has concealed a listening device in a daffodil in a vase of flowers on the desk of Colonel Von Strohm.'

'Apart from the satisfaction he obtains from dressing in girls' clothes,' asked Lieutenant Gruber, 'why would he do this?'

It appears that Herr Flick suspects General Von Klinkerhoffen and the Colonel of being involved in a plot to blow up Hitler. If it is true and the Colonel is tortured we will all be implicated because he may reveal that Lieutenant Gruber is painting a forgery of The Fallen Madonna with the Big Boobies and the Van Gogh with the Big Daisies.

Our only hope is that Lieutenant Gruber can warn the Colonel, who has been busily engaged today acquiring novelties for the party to celebrate Goering's birthday.

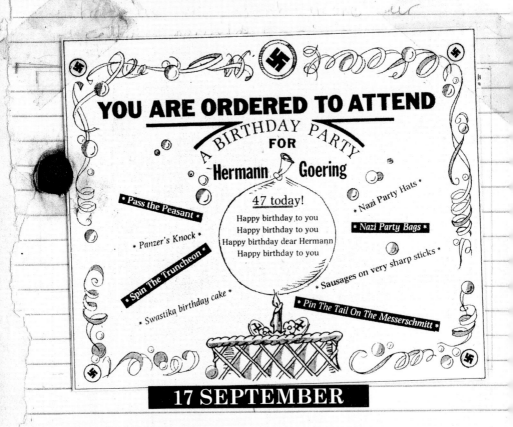

Good news from Lieutenant Gruber. He managed to warn the General about Herr Flick, and 'Irma Von Kinkenrotten' has been arrested and thrown into a dungeon in the château.

Bad news from Michelle of the Resistance. A radio message was due tonight from London, which meant that two volunteers had a lot of pedalling to do on the tandem in the bedroom of my wife's mother. Yvette stepped forward at once and offered her services. She was wearing a silk athletics singlet that was two sizes too small, and very flimsy shorts. I jumped into the saddle behind her at once, eager to let my thighs do their bit for France.

'Your breath is very hot,' she said to me as I pedalled like a mad hamster.

'Your shorts are very thin,' I replied.

19 SEPTEMBER

Fairly quiet day, today. Got up. Got dressed. Got arrested. It seems the Colonel is very cross about the batteries stolen from the German midget submarine.

Edith launched an attempt to rescue me, disguised as a German soldier, but as she left the café, the Itie Bertorelli turned up and Edith had to dive into the pissoir to avoid him. The Itie also went into the pissoir. It was when he left that I, having masterfully negotiated my release with the Colonel so that I could live to fight another day for the glory of France, arrived.

As you can imagine, Edith was overjoyed to be reunited with the bravest man in all France. She presented me with the hand grenade she had been intending to use in her rescue bid. But not before she had taken the pin as a souvenir. I looked at it. I looked at Edith. We looked at each other. We got out of there faster than the British off the beaches of Dunkirk. Seconds later, the convenience blew sky-high. This is going to cause quite a stink, I can tell you.

Anyway, there is rather a pungent postscript to all this business. As I went back to check for survivors and to prevent looting, I discovered amongst the wreckage several envelopes addressed to England. Sadly, the letters

Dear Mummy

I say, Mumsy, Fairfax is a bit down in the old mouth just now.

We got a right old wigging from Smelly Gibson on the Froggies' radio. Seems if we don't escape soon the war will be over. Smelly says we're doing rather badly against the Jerries and it's all costing an awful lot so he's stopped our pay. I say, that's a bit of a rum do, don't you think?

Then Smelly gave Fairfax more bad news. "Your fiancé is getting married on Thursday," he said.

"Deirdre? I can't be back by then," said Fairfax.

"She's marrying Randy Hargreaves. Any message?"

"Yes. Tell her to get stuffed!"

"It's a bit late for that."

Oh well, Mumsy, I'll write again soon. Hope this finds you as it leaves me,

Over and out,

Your loving son,

Carstairs

P.S. Any chance of burping over the odd franc now they've stopped all my tuck money?

P.P.S. Still no news from you. Are you sure you've got the address right?

are all in English so I don't understand a word of them. What they were doing there is a total mystery to me.*

* *This entry clears the air on an issue that English war historians have been straining over ever since the publication in 1946 of the wartime reminiscences of Monsieur Alfonse, The Wooden Hearse. The mystery was over the non-arrival in England of all the letters which the two British airmen had faithfully posted home to their mothers every Sunday evening. Alfonse wrote of Carstairs' bemusement that 'here in Froggie land the chaps don't seem averse to the odd tinkle in a pillar-box'. Now at last it is clear. They thought the pissoir was for posting letters in.*

6 OCTOBER

Helga was very pleased with herself today. Herr Flick, now out of the clink, feels that she has shown great devotion by helping him to perfect his interrogation techniques and has presented her with the Gestapo Certificate of Merit. It is not only a great honour, but with it she can get into the cinema free before five o'clock.

8 OCTOBER

Yvette and Mimi have hatched a plot to steal some film for Michelle's spy camera. Yvette has invited the Colonel to take photographs of her in her underwear, and Mimi will steal the film from the Colonel's camera while Yvette is distracting him with the flying helmet and wet celery. What I wouldn't give to be there myself.*

Michelle has disguised the spy camera as a large potato. Next time they order food from the château I am to deliver it. Then I must get into the room containing the safe and take a photograph so that Monsieur Leclerc, the ex-jailbird, can work out how we can break into it and steal the invasion plans. I will then deliver the film to Monsieur Alfonse, who has, in his mortuary, many fluids which skilfully blended can develop the film.

I tell you, I wish I had stayed with the girls in the typing pool.

* *Can one ever cease to marvel at the bravery of this man? No sooner has René escaped from one close shave than he is willing to risk his life all over again in yet another dangerous situation.*

9 OCTOBER

Today General Von Klinkerhoffen decided to let his hair down. He ordered Lieutenant Gruber to arrange a date for him with Helga this evening at the café. Which might have been all right had Herr Flick of the Gestapo not arrived just before the General ...

Everyone in the café fell silent as Flick limped in.

'There is no reason to cease your jollification just because a senior Gestapo officer in a particularly foul mood is entering your premises,' he said. Then he spotted Helga.

'So – there you are. What kind of funny old game is this? I have two tickets for a film featuring Herr Stanley Laurel and Herr Oliver Hardy and I am left waiting in the foyer holding a bag of chocolate fudge ...'

'I am sorry, Herr Flick. I have been ordered by General Von Klinkerhoffen to be his companion for the evening.'

'You will learn, Helga, that nobody stands up the Gestapo.'

'Oh Herr Flick – to see you consumed with jealousy is most stimulating.'

'I am not consumed with jealousy. I am just mad as a snake. You will leave with me now.'

'I cannot. I am obeying orders.'

'I thought that you and I had something good going ...'

To cut a long story short, Herr Flick has arrested Helga and taken her away for lengthy questioning. And Yvette has been taken away by the Colonel with a lengthy bit of celery.

12 OCTOBER

Mission accomplished. I have risked life and limb in the château and a lot more in Gruber's bedroom – but I have the photograph of the safe.

We set off last night as planned. Monsieur Alfonse took us there in his small hearse with the small horse and the big taxi-meter. As an inspiration to the others I chose to sit right up at the front, out in the open. Away from the smell of embalming fluid.

'We think the safe is in a room on the first floor,' Michelle briefed me as she handed forward the camera which was disguised as a potato. 'Deliver the food to the kitchen. Go to the room quickly. Photograph the safe and run like the clappers.'

'The last bit will be easy,' I said. I sometimes find that a little quip like this can do wonders for the troops' morale. 'But what do I say if I get caught?' Not for the first time, I felt it my job as commander to draw up a contingency plan that would buy valuable time for the others in the event of my capture.

'Say you are going to a Bring-Your-Own-Potato party.'

Really, that girl will be the death of us all. That is, if the RAF don't get there first. Leclerc intercepted us at that point to say he'd received a message on the wireless that they were going to bomb the German troops in Nouvion. To Edith this was excellent news. She said I should be proud to be bombed by them. Little did she realise, we are not insured against the RAF.

'Go back and tell them to keep well clear of the café,' I told the old fool. 'Tell them we will shine a torch up the chimney.'

No sooner had we arrived back in town than the British raid went ahead. If only they had known that in the pocket of the bravest man in all France was a potato containing a camera containing a picture of a safe containing the plans for the German invasion of England they would probably have tried not to hit me.

Unfortunately they did not know this. Perhaps, I thought, I should try to signal to them with my torch.

'Put out that lit or you will be shat on the spit,' shouted a policeman.

'Officer Crabtree,' I pleaded, 'can you not explain to your English friends that we are on their side? If I am killed it will be the end of the Resistance in this part of France.' Well, certainly in the doorway where I was standing.

RAF BOMB
BALL- BEARING FACTORY

Germans claim 43 Brits shot down – but we find no trace

'All pieces picked up very quickly' says Von Klinkerhoffen

'Bummers show plenty of fart left in earmen' says police eyewitness

In last night's massive raid by RAF bombers on the German ball-bearing factory at Nouvion, only two local casualties have so far been reported. One worker who lost his bearings, and another who lost his b

'You should be grateful that the RAF bummers are still farting for freedom,' he said.

There's not a lot you can say to that, is there?

15 OCTOBER

The old undertaker with the dicky ticker has developed the film in his embalming fluids and the old fool Leclerc has identified the make of the safe. I briefed Michelle to come up with a plan to get us into Gruber's room tonight so Leclerc can carry out a blow-job.

Michelle decided it would be a good idea to drop a smokebomb down Gruber's chimney. This will cause him to vacate the room. I hope that's all the scare will cause him to vacate. I will then smash in his window disguised as a fireman and enter with the geriatric geligniter, Leclerc – also disguised as a fireman.

Before I had time to comment on this brilliant stratagem, the idiot Crabtree arrived. He was walking very gingerly. 'I am sorry that I am lit,' he said, 'I had to wik curfully down the stroot because I have five fit of fuse wound round my log, and detonators dingling down my troosers.'

...ger and out,
your loving son
Fairfax

P.S Please tell Nanny my bowels are open again.

Needless to say, Michelle's masterplan blew up in her face. Or rather, my face. She and Edith dropped the smokebomb down the wrong chimney, and when I smashed my way into Gruber's bedroom there wasn't a puff in sight, apart from Gruber. Luckily, the General burst into the room at this moment and shouted 'Fire!'

Crabtree was on hand to give some expert advice. 'Depress the plinger and direct the nizzle at the muddle of the fear.'

'Get out of my way,' said Michelle as she pushed Gruber aside. 'I can spray this only once.'

Leclerc and I escaped from the château in Gruber's uniform and longcoat. We'd made it all the way back to the café when we saw Germans outside. Luckily there was a covered lorry to hide in until they went away. Unluckily, the lorry was full of members of the Communist Resistance.

'Oh, good evening,' I said pleasantly. 'You girls are probably wondering why we are dressed as German officers.'

'All German officers dress this way. Your French accent does not fool us for one moment. Put up your hands.'

'Look, you have got the wrong idea. We are French. Just go into the little café in there and ask.'

'Café René?' their leader spat. 'We are the Communist Resistance. We would not set foot in the café of that collaborator dog who entertains the Germans every night.'

'One day we will shoot him and hang his body from a lamp post,' said another. 'Now don't waste our time. What is your name?'

'Captain Von Smittelhoffen,' I replied.

'Excuse me,' said Leclerc, 'will you also shoot his pianist?'

'Of course.'

'Erich Von Beckstein at your service.'

Dear Mumsy

  Had another crack at giving ourselves up today, but the Krauts just aren't playing ball.

I went up to a Jerry officer and used some of that German I learnt at school. "Mein Herr," I said, "Vee the British airmen are. Give up very much we would like to."

Do you know what, Mumsy? The blighter swiped me on the knuckles with his cane. Just like old Stinky Blenkinsop used to when he took my trousers down in his study. Flaming Krauts. Don't even understand their own language. I tell you, Mumsy, if I wasn't writing to you first and therefore had a stamp left I'd jolly well write to Hitler and tell him what an absolute shower he's got here.

Still, chin up old thing. We're not going back to that Froggie camp our tails between our legs, I can tell you. We'd look a couple of right liarlies. Carstairs has had the wizard idea of commiting a crime and owning up to it. He's such a brick.

"What sort of crime?" I asked him.

"Well, how about chucking a brick through a shop window" he said.

"All right." I said, "off you go"

But the brick missed the window Mumsy and hit a Jerry on the helmet. I don't think that's a crime we'll own up to.

TFN - must scarper

Roger and out,

     Your loving son
        Fairfax

P.S Please tell Nanny my bowels are open again.

17 OCTOBER

It was Michelle who broke the sad news of my capture to Edith, Yvette and Mimi. By all accounts they took it very hard.

'Where are they holding him?' asked Yvette.

'That's rather a personal question,' Michelle replied.

'I am his wife,' said Edith, 'you can tell me. Where are they holding him?'

'In the old saw-mill east of Nouvion.'

'We will storm the saw-mill and rescue him,' said Mimi.

'Yes, we will storm the saw-mill and rescue him,' said Edith. 'How will we rescue him?'

'Outside is Gruber's little tank. We will steal it. If necessary we will use the big gun and blow them to pieces.'

'But they are Frenchmen,' Yvette protested.

'They are the wrong Frenchmen.'

'It is a good plan,' said Michelle. 'Go quickly.'

'Are you not coming?'

'I cannot – I have a dinner party for the Rouen Resistance. The stew is in the oven.'

And so it was that the three of them launched themselves in Gruber's little tank on a rescue mission to save the bravest man in all France, reversed into the new town pissoir, and nearly killed the policeman who was swinging his truncheon in one of the cubicles.

'There is obviously no piss for the wicked,' he said as he rose unsteadily from the wreckage.

Luckily I did not need their help to escape. I have been released and this is how easy it was: Denise Laroque, the former lion-tamer and now leader of the fanatical Communist Resistance, Nouvion West Sub-Area, was just about to whip my naked back when she spotted the perfect strawberry birthmark – even to the little stalk – that I acquired when I was born in a snowstorm and the doctor could not come out because he had Asian 'flu so Madame Triconfort, who was my mother's daily help, assisted at

CAFÉ RENÉ

dear friends in Avignon,

~~the town I should never have left~~, if you could see me now,
I would weep for a poor old starving woman.

...st to eat, I must pick camembert from the mousetraps with
...ezers. The mice are living better in my daughter's cafe then her
... old starving mother. All she brings me is gruel made from potatoe
...s and chicken bones. I would cry with self-pity into this soup, but
... weak enough already.

René has gone on a mission and has not returned. Do not weep,
dear friends in Avignon, the town I should never have left, he was
...orthless bum. My daughter should marry that undertaker now
...e is bananas about her.

"But he is too old," Edith tells me, she thinks only of herself. What
...ut my funeral? If she married him I could have a marble angel on
...tomb blowing a trumpet. I have the inscription all ready:

"How sad we are Mama's departed,
But we remember how she
From her birth destined for Heaven,
Now she's gone at ninety-seven."

...know I am only ninety-five, but never fear, I am hanging on
...make it rhyme.

Your poor old starving friend

Janny

R

Dear Mumsy,

Rather put my foot in it today, I'm afraid. We went to the Froggie police station and gave ourselves up to a Froggie officer who had his back turned to us at the time.

"We British airmen come from sky." I said in English, but loud enough for the Froggie to understand. "Shot down, with to give up."

"Are you mad?" he said, turning round. "It is every officer's duty to escape."

Good heavens, Mumsy, it was Crabtree, the British agent. Fairfax took a firm line with him at once. "Now listen, weren't you sent to get us back to England?"

"Well it's very difficult, don't you know there's a war on?" I thought I'd put in my tuppence worth while we were at it: "We've been here for ages and nothing seems to happen."

"Well to be perfectly honest," said Crabtree, we're not all satisfied with these De Gaulle Resistance people and we're thinking of taking our business elsewhere. The Communists seem to have more go in them."

Communists. Can you imagine it Mumsy? I said it would cost Daddy his seat if word got out.

"Parliament?"

"Wimbledon."

"I say, haven't you got a Liberal Resistance?" asked Fairfax.

"Yes," said Crabtree, "but he's in bed with the flu."

And we're still here in rotten old Froggie land.

Your loving son

Carstairs

P.S. Photo attached.

the confinement and used the tongs that were in the coal-bucket.

'I have seen this before,' Denise said. 'It was on the shoulder of my childhood sweetheart ... It was a hot August day on a riverbank in Nancy. The scent of the flowers in the field filled the air that we breathed. He was fishing. I sat beside him. He let me hold his worms. We kissed a tender kiss and the ice-cream that I was holding melted on his shirt.'

'Chocolate ripple,' I recalled.

'Correct. He removed his shirt to cleanse it in the bubbling stream and for the first time I saw the mark – this mark. But his name was René Artois.'

'My name is René Artois ...'

From that moment, everything fell into place. I was able to explain all my brave exploits that I have carried out so cleverly under the guise of a cowardly café-owner, and we were in the clear.

There is only one problem though. Denise Laroque has decided that destiny has thrown us together. The Welfare Committee of the Communist Resistance has had a meeting. By a show of daggers they have decided that she will be allowed to marry me and the wedding can take place on Saturday.

'We will commandeer the church of St Paul in the Rue de Vallee. We will kidnap the priest and we will break into the dress-shop of Madame Lenare and steal the wedding dress which is displayed in her window. For you, a wedding suit and top hat will be acquired by forcing the back door of the five-hundred-franc tailors in the High Street.'

It seems all the normal things have been taken care of. Who will be doing the catering, I wonder – or will it just be sandwiches on the run?

'You have a good week blowing things up and we'll meet at the church on Saturday,' I said to her.

A sixth sense tells me Edith is not going to be happy about all this.

18 OCTOBER

It appears from what Yvette tells me that several plots are being hatched by those who love and adore me to save me from the clutches of the Communist Resistance.

'If René marries Denise Laroque,' Edith said to Michelle, 'he will join the Communist Resistance and you will lose the services of the bravest man in all France.'

'I agree. He is our hero. We made him. The credit must not go to the loony left.'

'I have a plan,' my wife went on. 'Denise will be stealing her bridal gown from the dress shop of Madame Lenare. It is the one in the window with the thick veil. While she is doing this your people must kidnap her. I will take her place at the altar. Once René is married to me she can never wed him, because despite being a ruthless, murdering, bombing blackmailer, she is a good Catholic.'

Needless to say, I am to be kept in complete ignorance of this ...

21 OCTOBER

Edith walked into the bathroom while I was shaving this morning. No problem, except that Yvette had just been giving me a message* and had shaving soap on her face.

'Why has that serving girl got on her face shaving soap?' my inquisitive little wife wanted to know.

'Edith,' I said, 'have you no feelings? This poor shy slip of a girl has in her veins strong peasant blood. As a result

---

* *A prime example of just how vigilant an editor must be. In René's original handwriting, this word might easily have been mistaken for 'massage', which of course would have made no sense at all. It is quite obvious that what happened was that my mother delivered a message from the Resistance that was so secret, she had to whisper it in René's ear. In the process, she ended up with shaving soap on her face – and a free shave from Edith into the bargain.*

of this she grows a moustache every three months. This has hitherto been kept a secret. You come blundering in and in twenty-four hours the whole village will hold her up to ridicule.'

'Oh René, I swear I will say nothing. Poor child. René, give me the razor, you have missed a bit . . .'

22 OCTOBER

Imagine my surprise tonight when instead of opening the café as usual Edith laid on a little surprise for me. Yvette told me why she had done so later in the larder when we were canning noodles.*

'I have prepared for him to have a romantic candlelit dinner,' Edith had said to her and Mimi. 'It is for me to say to him one last fond farewell before he marries another.'

'It is terrible,' Yvette agreed. 'With that Laroque woman he will be dead within one week.'

'Unless the bullets get him first,' said Mimi.

I was taken aback to see Edith appear in such a nice dress. 'Does this mean you are to try out a new cabaret on your unsuspecting public?' I asked. But Edith led me into the back room. The table was set with candles, and there were many flowers and cards.

'See, there are candles, there are flowers,' she said. 'You know what this means?'

'Your mother is dead.'

'No, do you not recall? This is just how the table was set for dinner the first night of our honeymoon. I have planned that we should end our life together just as we started it.'

---

* *A pity about the smudged ink on these words. At first glance they appear to be saying 'canoodling', but it is clear to me that the correct interpretation is the one I have chosen to print, which concerns food preparation in the cellar.*

'We are not committing suicide, are we?'

'You are overwrought, René,' said Edith, and she was right.

As I sat down, she handed me the napkin as she had done that night. On the table were all the cards that our friends had sent to us to wish us good luck and happiness.

'Now,' Edith said, 'a little wine. It is the same wine

As René himself often said: 'Give me the tool and I'll finish the job.'

that we drank that night.'

'Ah, lucky we remembered to put the cork back in.'

Then it all started to come back to me in a tidal wave of memories. Edith was sixteen, the prettiest looking girl in the street. Come to think of it, she was the only girl in the street.

'Dear Edith, you are very sweet. I do not deserve you – perhaps I never did. Here I am about to marry another and you are being so brave. You are reminding me of all the things about you that I shall miss. You have arranged everything as it was all those years ago. The flowers, the candles, the table – all as it was in that little private room in that little hotel.'

'And there is one other thing that is the same . . .'

'The bill?'

'No.' She rang a little bell. In came her mother, dressed as a Nippy girl waitress. It was not the most erotic of sights.

'Oh yes, I forgot. Your mother got us a special rate because she worked there.'

The old crone poured us some soup.

'I have prepared the same menu,' said Edith. 'We dined, we drank, we talked, we went to bed in each other's arms and as the clock struck twelve . . .'

'Consommé,' said her mother.

'No,' I said, 'not that night.'

Yvette and Mimi, bless them, have hatched a plot of their own. It involves interfering with the priest at my wedding.

I will not write any more. I must get my sleep. Tomorrow night is going to be one of the biggest of my life. I have a reputation for being the hardest man in all France. I only hope I can keep it up.

As I write this entry, dear Diary, Edith is over there at the window table gently weeping. The reason is as follows. When, yesterday afternoon, I was at the point of twenty guns in the process of marrying Denise Laroque, the Head of the Communist Resistance, Nouvion Division, Edith, bravely or stupidly, depending on your viewpoint, substituted herself for Denise in the hope of becoming my bride. Little did she know that my waitresses, who both

ARCH OF CROSSED DAGGERS AT NOUVION WEDDING

The wedding took place on Saturday afternoon of M. René Artois, the popular owner of the Café René, and Mme Denise Laroque, the fanatical ex-lion tamer, now leader of the Communist Resistance (Nouvion West Sub-Area).

The groom wore a traditional wedding suit with trousers that were tight under the arms. The bride was resplendent in a thick veil.

Best Man was Monsieur Alfonse. Those in attendance included: Colonel Von Strohm and Lieutenant Gruber (in plain clothes with bowler hats); many peasants; several pretty girls who were crying; many grim-faced girls of the Communist Resistance, and Michelle of the ordinary Resistance.

The bride walked down the aisle to the tune of the Red Flag, and as everyone is equal with the Communists, she gave herself away.

Specially present for the occasion was one of the Church's most senior clerics.

'We are gathered togother in the presence of Gid,' he began, 'to jane this women and this min in Haly Weedlock.'

Apparently these Roman Catholic services are always conducted in Latin.

Organist: Monsieur Leclerc Choir members included: Fraulein Helga Geerhart (mezzo soprano); Herr Otto Flick (sinister baritone). Chief Mourners: Mme Yvette, Mme Mimi.

have the hots for me, had substituted Crabtree the idiot
English agent for the Catholic priest.*

This means of course that the wedding was not legal
(a) because he was not a proper priest and (b) because
even the good Lord himself could not have understood one
word of the ceremony, which due to his atrocious French
accent was fortunately presumed by Lieutenant Gruber
and the other guests to be in Latin.

28 OCTOBER

My fanatical childhood sweetheart kills any man who
rejects her. Who will she blame for this fiasco? Me –
because I told everyone of the wedding plans. It is little
consolation that she is apparently safely held up in the
bottom of a mine shaft by Michelle of the Resistance. What
happens if she escapes? How will I carry on the fight for
liberty if I have been gunned down by a jealous ex-lover?

'We will keep her there until after the war,' says Edith.
'I will send sandwiches down.'

Yes, and with any luck they'll hit her on the head. A
glancing blow from one of Edith's spam and lettuce
doorsteps would give her something to think about all
right. I should know, I was on the receiving end of one last
year when Edith caught me on the billiard table showing
Yvette how to go in off, and my actions were totally
misinterpreted. I still needed massage a fortnight later.

'With your reputation, Monsieur, it will be assumed
that she is too exhausted to resume guerrilla warfare,'
said Monsieur Alfonse helpfully.

'What reputation?' Edith wanted to know.

'It is all part of the myth, Edith,' I tried to explain.

---

* *It is an enigma to me why René should choose this moment to mention
that both Yvette and Mimi appear to have successfully purchased for
him a pair of heated hostess trolleys.*

'Word of mouth exaggerates little things into big things. I blow up a bus station, it becomes an ammunition factory. You know how it is. But you are all to blame. Perhaps this will teach you to consult me before putting into effect your idiot plans.'

Just think, dear Diary. Denise Laroque has been shafted! She will not like this. I can see her right now, scraping at the earth with her bare hands, spitting my name between clenched teeth. What happens if she finds a shovel? Oh my God, I wish I hadn't thought of that.

'The mine shaft is a mile deep . . .' said Edith comfortingly.

A mile deep. Is that all?

3 NOVEMBER

Michelle of the Resistance came to see me today and added to my concern.

'What are you doing here?' I demanded. 'You should be sitting on a big slab of stone on top of the mine shaft.'

'The slab of stone is still in place.'

'Thank heavens.'

'Unfortunately, Denise found a shovel.'

I knew it! Apparently she tunnelled into an adjacent shaft, and though the guard followed her through a labyrinth of tunnels and passages, she outpaced him and fled, spitting my name through her clenched teeth.

'Oh my God. Well, that is it. Yvette – my hat and coat.'

I was going to give myself up to the Germans. It was the only way to keep myself alive to fight for France another day. I would tell them I stole their painting. They would put me in jail, of course, but with good conduct I should be out in a few years, by which time Denise would with any luck have blown herself up.

But just as I was about to leave, the café door burst

Dear Mumsy,

    I am a caged lion. I can't stand being cooped up in a police station much longer. I have an idea running round my head - I'll trip it out and see what you think.

There's always a little tank parked outside the cafe. Why don't Carstairs and I dress up as krauts and steal it? I drove Daddy's Austin Seven once. Must be the same principle. We could fight our way to the coast, bash into the docks, hijack a submarine and poodle across to England.

I hope you think more of the plan than Carstairs did. When I put it to him all he did was wish me good luck. Seems he's not coming with me.

    Roger and out
        Your loving son
            Fairfax

open. A girl with a machine gun leapt inside and sprayed the bar with bullets. I fell down behind the bar at once, stone dead.

Only pretending, of course. But since I'd managed to escape the bullets it seemed to make a lot of sense to stay where I was – lying under Yvette and Mimi.

I have spent the rest of the day disguised as my own father, seeking asylum from the Germans, the Gestapo and the gendarmes.

'The fanatical head of the Communist Resistance is trying to kill me!' I said to the Colonel and Lieutenant Gruber.

'You will get used to it,' said the Colonel. 'They are trying to kill us all the time.'

Herr Flick of the Gestapo did not exactly embrace the role of protector with open arms, either.

'Could you not keep me in a dungeon for a few days until the heat is off?' I pleaded.

'*We* pick the people we lock up,' he said.

And as for the gendarmerie! I went there and rang the bell for several minutes before a policeman appeared.

'Will you please stop bonging the bill,' he said. 'Or I shall lick you up for disturbing the puss. Are you confessing to some cream? In that curse you must fill in a foam.'

But it turned out that all the cills were filled to copocity anyway. My only hope would be to come back next woke. Oh my God. Why do I pay rates?

I got back to the café only to find myself the victim of a poisoned wine attack by the Communist Resistance. It was the final straw. I resolved to head at once for the station. Until the dust settles here, there must be a vacancy for a cuckoo clock salesman in Switzerland.

I left the café a desperate man. The next thing I knew, I was being escorted into the back of a Communist Resistance lorry to be reunited with my erstwhile bride, Denise Laroque.

'I know the truth,' she said. Much to my surprise she did not spit, as she spoke, through clenched teeth. 'In a fit of pique I tried to have you shot only to discover that you were blameless. It is the women of the café that I should kill.'

'Well, of course, it was their fault, but is killing not a little drastic? I am sure they would apologise, pay you nominal damages.'

Denise's response was to grab me and crush her lips against mine. She made me swear that I will never leave her again. I swore.

'Now – I have bad news,' she added. 'I must go to Lyon for the party conference. I have been nominated to be Party Chairman.'

'Oh dear,' I sighed, 'can you not get out of it?'

'No,' she said firmly. 'All is ready for me. The ballots have been rigged. The moderates are under lock and key. The democratic process must take its course. But I will return for revenge – and for love.'

I can hardly wait.

5 NOVEMBER

I have had to break the bad news to the women in my life that they are on the hit list of the fanatical Denise Laroque. She has vowed to kill them all. Edith first.

Edith did not take it well.

'Right, that is it,' she said, going to the till and taking out all the money. 'The Spanish border cannot be that far away. If I walk all night and crawl all day I could be there by Christmas.'

'Edith, you will never get to the end of the street. The Communists have gun-persons everywhere.'

'Then I will disguise myself.'

And that was the last I have seen of her. Maybe there's something to be said for Karl Marx after all.

Michelle of the Resistance stole up my back passage again tonight and crept into the kitchen just as I was showing Yvette how I like to have my b ls fond ed.*

    'Michelle,' I said, 'it is not always convenient to have you barging in on my private moments. Could you not make an appointment?'

---

* *Another smudged entry that might be open to possible misinterpretation. The correct reading, however, since they are in the kitchen, appears to be that René is instructing Yvette as to how he likes to have his 'bols fondued'. I have been unable to trace any other reference in Normandy cookery books to what must be a peculiarly regional dish featuring the fiery Dutch liqueur, but it certainly sounds as though it would make your mouth water.*

'The German Generals will soon be meeting at the château to discuss plans for the invasion of England,' she carried on. 'Their maps will be on the table. Somehow we must photograph them.'

'Why are you telling me this?'

'Because you will be asked to do the catering.'

'How do you know?' I asked. 'There are three other catering firms in Nouvion.'

'Yours will be the lowest estimate or else the others will be burned down for collaborating.'

11 NOVEMBER

Poor Herr Flick. Helga tells me he has placed an advertisement in the local paper for a servant but he has had only one reply. It came through the window on a brick.

Single Gestapo gentleman requires willing and obedient peasant for menial domestic tasks. Apply to BOX 1, Gestapo HQ. Time wasters will be shot.

• Temporary • The Opposite Sex •

No hidden extras

If anyone is cheaper they will be shot

12 NOVEMBER

Would you believe it possible that the British have scaled new heights of madness?

Michelle burst into the back room this morning just as I was having a tiff with Mimi.*

'The RAF have dropped the bird that will carry the photographs back to England,' she said. 'It will be delivered today.'

'Well, for heaven's sake label it,' I said. 'My wife cooked the last pigeon for lunch.'

'It is not a pigeon. The Germans are shooting them down.'

'Then what is it?'

'It is a long-distance duck.'

'Now I have heard everything. Is this duck expected to fly all the way to England?'

'Should it become exhausted it will land on the English Channel and have a sleep. For this reason the photographs will be in waterproof containers.'

See what I mean?

* A reader less schooled in the character and ways of René Artois than I might easily be under the misguided impression here that instead of saying 'having a tiff' this partly smudged sentence actually says: 'having it off'. This is, of course, not only a blatantly outrageous suggestion, but a sickeningly unpatriotic one too. Just what the tiff was about, however, we are never told – testimony, surely, to René's outstanding powers of discretion when it comes to matters of staff relations.

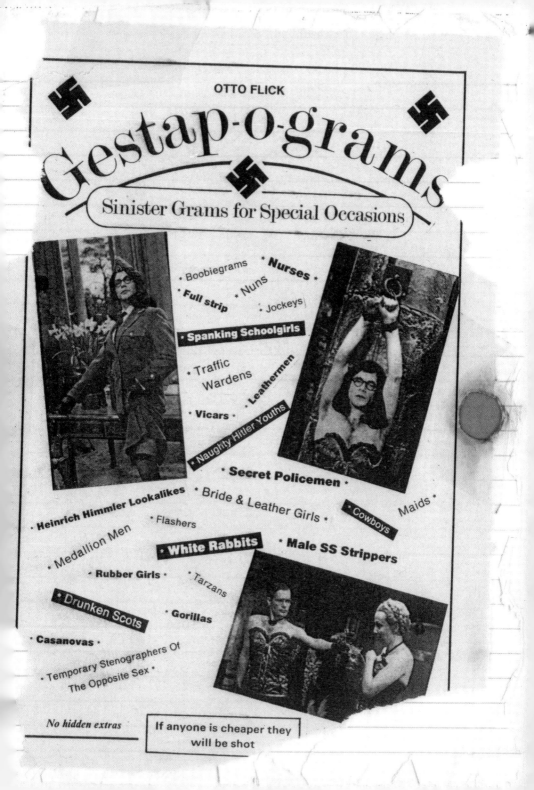

The Colonel wants to rescue the real paintings from their hiding place at the headquarters of the Communist Resistance. The Communists were armed to the teeth, I told him. They would be very dangerous.

'Could you not mount a military operation?' Helga asked. 'Say a company of infantry, some artillery and a few tanks, with a token amount of air cover?'

'No. The General might ask questions. We will have to be more sneaky than that – perhaps using only a handful of carefully selected ruthless men.'

'Providing we can find them!' quipped Lieutenant Gruber.

This comment drew a black look from the Colonel, but Gruber's bacon was saved by the entry at that moment of the Itie with the turkey feathers in his hat.

'Colonel-o, your old buddy Alberto Bertorelli is-a returned from Roma. See here – Mussolini, he give me a beautiful medal. In Roma I am given the finest crack troops in all-a Italy. Together we take-a the boats and we invade the British. I pick-a my men – each one with my own-a hand. They are the ruthless men.'

'Ruthless men?' I said. 'With respect, Colonel, I think this may be the answer to your problem ...'

'When can we meet them?' the Colonel asked.

'They wait-a for you to make-a the inspection. Come outside and say hallo.'

Outside in the town square were some of the scruffiest long-haired layabouts I have ever seen assembled in one place since Nouvion were at home to Port Vale in a pre-war friendly.* A complete shower. A shambles.

'Men, pay attention,' Gruber addressed the mob. 'I am Lieutenant Gruber – that is my little tank.'

'Oh – nice-a tank! Pretty!'

* *Nouvion won 3–0.*

'We have an assignment for you. North-east of this town is the headquarters of the Communist Resistance. We have important documents to recover from them. They are armed to the teeth and, like you, they are ruthless, desperate fighters.'

'To you will go the honour of attacking and defeating them,' said the Colonel.

'This is a great honour,' said Bertorelli. 'What do you say boys? Can-a we do it!'

To a man, the Ities scattered. Where once had stood the pride of Italy in their wide variety of ill-fitting uniforms, there was now only a pile of badly packed kit bags, half-eaten pizzas and a jar of Brylcreem.

Men after my own heart, I say.*

18 NOVEMBER

The German Generals begin their week-long meeting in the château tomorrow. They will be planning the invasion of England. The Resistance needs photographs of the maps.

'Michelle,' I enquired selflessly, 'this time, wouldn't you like to take the glory?'

'There will be no danger,' she said. 'We have devised a special apparatus which will not be visible.'

Oh yes, this apparatus will not be visible. Do you know what it consists of? A sort of jacket affair, with a false left arm that rests on the hip. This is to leave my left hand free to operate my apparatus. With the jacket is also an apron, beneath which is a camera.

---

*   *René appears to have misinterpreted the Italians' response. He is under the impression that they – as the bravest man in all France would have done in their place – have rushed off at once to carry out their deadly task. It would not have occurred to such a gallant fighter that the Italians had simply scarpered.*

The TATE GALLERY

VAN CLOMP

RETROSPECTIVE

The TATE GALLERY 1946

VAN CLOMP RETROSPECTIVE

The Van Clomp retrospective now showing for a limited season at the Tate Gallery offers a rare opportunity to re-assess this artist's unique features.

In any exhibition of Van Clomp's work, his extraordinary Fallen Madonna with the Big Boobies must inevitably provide the centrepieces. The eye is constantly drawn back to this canvas by the boldness of the brush-strokes, the sheer enormity of the vision. But it should not, nay cannot, obscure our appreciation of the other paintings assembled here for the first time by the Argentine-based fine art emporium of Gruber Geering Von Strohm.

True, certain basic themes are re-stated in La Madone Tombée avec les Boobies Grandes, and indeed in Zu Madonna mit das Grosses Boobies Gefallen. On closer inspection, however, the connoisseur will notice slight differences between the twelve or so works on display – subtle nuances of shade and line, of shape and colour, that can only enhance one's sense of wonder.

It is hardly surprising that they have been so long sought after, nor that they have without exception fallen into the hands of private collectors.

'How am I supposed to operate it?' I asked.

'Feel around and you will find a little knob. Have you got it?'

'I think so.'

'Pull it.'

I did. A small panel in the front of the apron lifted up, revealing a small camera and lens. There was a flash, then it disappeared again.

'Just think, René – with this you can save the world.'

I was speechless. If the future of civilisation as we know it depends upon the success of this device, is it a civilisation that is worth saving?

20 NOVEMBER

Leclerc has brought bad news. As he opened the hen-house door, the duck flew away. But he thinks he will not go far. He has not had his lunch.

Alfonse might save the day. He has duck-hunting equipment. Apparently, he used to stand in the river with an artificial duck on his head. Between his teeth he would hold his duck-quacker. He says that in his time he was famous for it. I am not surprised.

22 NOVEMBER

Alfonse and Leclerc spent the morning in the re-built pissoir together, with artificial ducks on their heads.

'Monsieur,' Leclerc asked Alfonse, 'why are we quacking here in the public convenience?'

'Because if the long-distance duck sees our bodies he will be put off. This way he will think we are two lady ducks. He will fly down and I will capture him with my fish-landing net.'

They were joined at this moment by the Itie, Bertorelli.

'Excusa that I ask,' said the Itie, 'but why do you wear on your head a duck?'

'We are trying to capture the duck that is quacking up

OCCUPIED
COUNTRY LIFE

VOL. XXXVIII   OCTOBER 1941

Fraulein Helga Geerhart, only daughter of Herr and
Frau Herman Geerhart of Stuttgart, who is engaged to
be married to Herr Otto Flick, whose family back-
ground is very exalted and is nobody's business.

there,' said Alfonse.

'For our dinner,' added Leclerc.

'Ah – I see. That a piece-a cake-a.'

And with that he took out his revolver and fired a shot into the sky. Out of the sky thudded a duck.

'Have a good dinner,' said Bertorelli.

24 NOVEMBER

I am taking pills to calm my nerves. I need them for many reasons. First, because I have just photographed the map of the German plan to invade England.

Also, because Lieutenant Gruber has just cruised in on a social call and he's wearing the perfume that is so popular with the Tank Corps, lily of the valley with a hint of diesel oil. By the glint in his eye, I'd say his sights were firmly set on opening up a second front before the night is out. I'm very keen that it shouldn't be mine.

The Resistance are at this moment developing the negatives in Monsieur Alfonse's embalming fluid. Fortunately, the Itie Bertorelli had missed the duck, but the poor animal collapsed out of the sky with shock. Now it is lying in a basket suffering from feather fatigue. It is in no condition to fly to England. I thought it best to take its temperature a few moments ago, so I shook the thermometer and shoved it into the duck's basket.

'It may have interrupted a nice dream,' said Edith with concern.

'It has probably started one,' I said.

'Come to think of it,' said the Lieutenant, 'I'm beginning to feel a little feverish myself.'

Dear Mumsy,

You know, the food here is absolutely [...]. It's a complete myth about French cooking being [...] best in the world, and the fact that we're in [...] it is no excuse. All you can taste is garlic. If we [...]ught one of the rats we could probably barbecue it [...]ver a candle.

Do you know, Mumsy, I've been thinking - it's about [...]ime those Americans came in. They saved us in the [...]ast war. If they don't hurry up there won't be any [...]ar left.

Fairfax is a bit down in the mouth again. He [...]ays if his mummy and daddy knew he was in jail they'd [...]ve a fit. I've told him not to worry - it's not going [...] be in the tatler, is it? He's worried that if it ever [...]omes out that he's got a prison record it could stop [...]im getting a decent job after the war. I asked him what he's going to do and he says he's going into the Stock Exchange, so that's all right isn't it - they won't mind.

Well, must go now to bribe a guard or someone to smuggle this out for me.

Roger and out,
Your loving jailbird (ha! ha!) son,

Carstairs

P.S. Will the garlic be all right for my spots Mumsy? I don't want the other boys laughing at me when I get back to the squadron.

P.P.S. Photo attached.

25 NOVEMBER

Today I resigned from the Resistance. I am no longer a member. If Michelle thinks I'm incompetent just because I took a photograph of a map that the Germans hadn't yet marked she can take her duck and her radio and find someone else to be the bravest man in all France.

26 NOVEMBER

Today I am back in the Resistance. Last night Michelle slipped secretly up my back passage and refused to accept my resignation.

'I cannot go on without you,' she said. 'I love you. I always have and until the end of time I always will.'

So that is settled. After talks lasting just under two hours in the back room, I put my major point on the table and pushed it home hard. Michelle seemed quietly impressed. I have now seen everything from another angle. I am back in my old position.*

28 NOVEMBER

Lieutenant Gruber and two stormtroopers popped into the café tonight, with orders to arrest me. General Von Klinkerhoffen thinks that I am responsible for trying to poison everyone at the Generals' meeting at the château. Hence I am writing this in the cupboard in the bedroom of my wife's mother. In the dark. It seems imperative to me that the Resistance is not deprived of its leader at this

---

* *We'll probably never know the exact nature of René's negotiating instrument, nor the full scope of his demands. Knowing René, money alone would not have come into it. Far more likely is that he was hanging out for improved satisfaction on the job.*

crucial stage of the war. My one regret about going into hiding is the terrible smell that seems to hang around this room, like stale onion soup. Perhaps a mouse has died.

29 NOVEMBER

I am going to make a run for it, disguised as a French General with a big hooter. Leclerc has modelled me one out of plastic explosive. It will not go off unless I light the wick, which is buried in my nostril. Thank heavens I do not smoke. Or pick my nose.

To create a diversion in the café Yvette is going to tempt the Colonel upstairs with a special end-of-season offer – wet rhubarb. This will enable me to walk out of the front door, turn left, and head for Spain. My fondest hope is that I'll be able to maintain my affairs from such a long distance away. And that Yvette will understand why it was essential for me to pull out so early.

30 NOVEMBER

I gave Yvette one last fond embrace in the cellar this morning and walked upstairs. Unfortunately, the Colonel and Gruber were waiting at the bar.

'Ah, General!' called the Colonel. 'How good to see you. Come to our table and take some wine. It is so good to have you on our side.'

'I am sorry, Colonel, I cannot,' I said. 'I have an urgent appointment to do some collaborating.'

'Colonel,' he said, 'it is René under an assumed nose.'

Unfortunately the assumed nose was tickling me, and I sneezed. I didn't realise that the wick was then left dangling from my nostril, and everyone was too polite to tell me. The three of us put our heads together conspiratorially over the candle to discuss the paintings of The Fallen Madonna with the Big Boobies by Van Clomp and the Cracked Vase with the Big Daisies by Van Gogh.

'René,' the Colonel said, 'your nose is smouldering.'

Oh my God! Seizing the nose with both hands, I tore it off and ran to the door of the café. Edith opened it and I threw the highly explosive hooter out into the street in the nick of time. There was the sound of a big explosion.

'I apologise for my mother,' said Edith to the Colonel. 'She is ninety-five, you know.'

But just then Herr Flick appeared at the door. His leather coat and hat were in tatters and his stick was splayed. He took just two paces inside the café, spun on one heel and passed out.

2 DECEMBER

Lieutenant Gruber has informed General Von Klinkerhoffen that a French General attempted to assassinate Herr Flick of the Gestapo by exploding him. He now suspects the Vichy official of being the miscreant who tried to kill everyone at the meeting in the château. The finger of suspicion therefore no longer points at me. I am a free man!

'Whatever you want here will be on the house, Lieutenant,' said Edith.

'As long as it is on the menu,' I added.

Herr Flick is recovering in bed in his cellar. His arm is in a splint and tied to the roof in a 'Heil Hitler' position. One leg is suspended on a pulley.

Helga tells me she went to visit him a little earlier.

'It is terrible to see you like this, Herr Flick,' she said. 'Has any vital organ received damage?'

'I am testing them one at a time,' he replied.

4 DECEMBER

You may be wondering, dear Diary, why it is that you are down in the cellar of my café and why I am bricking myself up. I will tell you. Last night ten German Generals were planning the invasion in my café. To avoid being blown up by the Resistance they were disguised as French onion-sellers. Unfortunately they became mixed up with a lot of British airmen, also, of course, disguised as French onion-sellers. Thanks to the Resistance they are now on their way to the coast in a fish-truck to be taken by submarine to England. Naturally I will be blamed, so I intend to remain down here behind this wall till after the war.

5 DECEMBER

Edith has brought me two bottles of my favourite cognac and some more baked beans.

'Edith, I already have eight cases of baked beans – have you nothing else?'

'Here is a gorgonzola and some candles.'

'I think in the circumstances it will be better if they remain unlit.'

6 DECEMBER

Edith now wants to join me. She says that if the Germans can't find me, they will blame her. Yvette thinks that if the Germans can't find Edith, they will blame her. She, too, wants to join me.

'There is not enough room!' Edith protested. 'We will have to sleep on top of each other.'

'We must not be selfish, Edith,' I said.

TO: HERR OTTO FLICK
FROM: GESTAPO LOVED ONES' ANTI-HANKY-PANKY DEPARTMENT

TRANSCRIPT OF CONVERSATION BETWEEN LIEUTENANT HUBERT GRUBER AN
THE SUSPECT, PRIVATE HELGA GEERHART, RECORDED BY POWERFUL GEST
LISTENING DEVICE NO. 443/D, WHICH IN THE OFFICE OF THE SECRETA
OF COLONEL VON STROHM IS LOCATED.

SUSPECT: I have just made some coffee. Would you like some?
GRUBER: You are most kind. Very few people are kind to me a
          the moment. I find this most touching.
SUSPECT: You look pale Lieutenant.
GRUBER: Well, I'm not really cut out for all this war like
          activity you know. True, I have some affection for
          little tank but I don't wish to become attached to i
          I will have to hand it back when the war is over, wi
          I not?
SUSPECT: We all have to find what consolation we can in our
          unfamiliar roles. Take me for instance. The materi
          of my uniform has a coarse and unyielding texture bu
          I find it quite erotic. Unfortunately when it rains
          colour runs all over my underwear.
GRUBER: I miss the carefree life of a window dresser. It wa
          wonderful. I could position the models exactly as I
          wished. Then I could watch the passers-by press the
          noses to the glass. Sometimes when I had finished t
          would applaud.
SUSPECT: Have courage, Lieutenant Gruber. There will be wind
          after the war.
GRUBER: Not many.

7 DECEMBER

First the good news. The fish-lorry hit a bomb crater and all the German Generals are on their way back to Berlin. Now at least they will not know that they were being driven to the coast to be shipped off to England. They will simply think they were being driven to safety from the air-raid.

Now for the bad news. Gruber tells me that Berlin is blaming General Von Klinkerhoffen for the whole fiasco and General Von Klinkerhoffen is blaming the Colonel. The Colonel is bound to look for a scapegoat. I'm not absolutely sure what a scapegoat looks like, but I expect he will have a moustache, be slightly thinning on top, and will run a pleasant café in the Nouvion area of Normandy.

11 DECEMBER

Lieutenant Gruber came into the café in some distress tonight. He arrived in his little tank as usual, but I could tell by the grinding of the gears that he was out of sorts. It is not like him to have trouble finding reverse.

'It's a rather special friend, René ... he has been badly wounded.'

'That's terrible, Lieutenant. Where was he hit?'

'In the Bulge.'

'Very painful. Can I be of any assistance?'

'Thank you, René. Just lend me your support.'

'Of course, Lieutenant. Borrow *both* my supports if you think they will help ...'

14 DECEMBER

The Colonel wants the Itie Bertorelli to help him and
Gruber escape to Italy. With his connections in Rome they
can arrange to hide out in the Vatican. But it will take
money. Lots of money. The sort of money you can only
raise by selling paintings of The Fallen Madonna with the
Big Boobies by Van Clomp and the Cracked Vase with the
Big Daisies by Van Gogh.

'What about Helga?' Lieutenant Gruber asked the
Colonel. 'We promised to cut her in.'

'We will cut her out. They do not like women at the
Vatican.'

'Is there any chance of getting there for Christmas?'
the Lieutenant said.

15 DECEMBER

Lieutenant Gruber tells me that the Itie Bertorelli has his
doubts about the Colonel's plan.

'Colonel-o,' he said, 'I have to tell you that big boobies


```
                                        ... The mater:
                           ... and unyielding texture bu
                      ... erotic.  Unfortunately when it rains
                ...our runs all over my underwear.
GRUBER:    I miss the carefree life of a window dresser.  It wa
           wonderful.  I could position the models exactly as I
           wished.  Then I could watch the passers-by press the
           noses to the glass.  Sometimes when I had finished tl
           would applaud.
SUSPECT:   Have courage, Lieutenant Gruber.  There will be wind
           after the war.
GRUBER:    Not many.
```

cut no ice with the Pope.'

Michelle, of course, has other ideas. 'The Resistance need the paintings to sell for the Party funds,' she told me. 'You should take the forgeries, go to the headquarters of the Communist Resistance and substitute them so that the Germans will think that they have recovered the originals.'

'How could I do this? They have look-outs. Everyone who approaches will be shot.'

'They will not shoot a Franciscan friar wheeling a pram.'

Well, that would be an unusual sight, I had to admit. Especially with Mimi inside the pram dressed up as a baby. And even more so when the Franciscan friar wheeling his pram is shadowed at a distance of no more than a hundred metres or so by a mobile Gestapo observation unit consisting of Helga disguised as a nanny and Herr Flick curled up cosily inside with his gun in a dolly.

Resistance Weekly
Caption competition

"LISTEN VERY CAREFULLY, I SHALL SAY THIS ONLY ONCE."

"BAD NEWS FROM THE FRONT?"

"YOU COULD SAY THAT. ONE OF MY GIRLS HAS BEEN WOUNDED IN THE BREST AREA....."

This weeks winner – R. ARTOIS OF NOUVION

16 DECEMBER

Guess what popped out of the woodwork as soon as we had located the real paintings and swopped them over with the forgeries? Six highly-armed Communist girls and Denise Laroque, their highly-sexed leader.

'René Artois – my lover, my childhood sweetheart! You have returned to me as I knew that you would.'

'Hello,' I said. 'How was Lyon?'

She did not have a chance to tell me. At that moment shots rang out all around us. We were being stormed by Lieutenant Gruber in his little tank, with the Colonel, Edith, Yvette, Mimi and Monsieur Leclerc all in tow, and the Itie Bertorelli's hand-picked band of ruthless warriors. Seconds later, the white flag went up. Bertorelli had surrendered.

Any ideas on what I do next, dear Diary?

Here I am in the headquarters of the Communist Resistance, with no means of escape and everyone who might have come to my rescue also captured. All the paintings of The Fallen Madonna with the Big Boobies by Van Clomp and the Cracked Vase with the Big Daisies by Van Gogh are now in the hands of the Communists. The café is supposed to open at six and there is no one to run it. And as if all that wasn't enough, I've just run out of pages in this diary.*

---

* *It is perhaps just as well that René has run out of space. As my mother never tired of telling me, if the great man could be said to have had one outstanding feature it was a tendency to be over-length.*

One cannot help wondering what the missing sections of his diary would have revealed, but one thing is beyond doubt – it can never be said that René Artois did not have a hard war.

GESTAPO INC.
BERLIN

Dear Otto,

I am most displeased with your lack of progress. Hitler still does not have the painting of the Fallen Madonna with the Big Boobies which he promised to Eva for her birthday, and you have provided no evidence of the plot to blow up the Fuhrer. What is more you have so far cost us two staff cars, one blown up and one flattened by a steam-roller.

What sort of a Gestapo are you running up there? Get your act together or you could find yourself limping around the Russian Front.

Your affectionate uncle,

HEINY

Gestapo is a registered trademark of the Nazi Party
Managing Director: H Himmler
Cables SINISTER BERLIN

HEADQUARTERS OF THE COMMUNIST RESISTANCE

NOUVION WEST SUB AREA

As you can see, Comrade Diary, there are going to be a few
changes around here from now on.